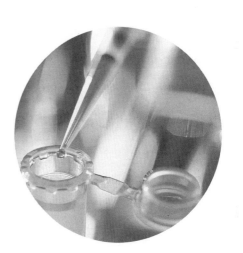

IGCSE
Study Guide

for Chemistry

Bob Berry

HODDER
EDUCATION
AN HACHETTE UK COMPANY

The Publishers would like to thank the following for permission to reproduce copyright material:

Photos Figures 1.1a–d Andrew Lambert
Examination questions Question 1 p. 92 is reproduced by permission of the University of Cambridge Local Examinations Syndicate.

Every effort has been made to trace all copyright holders, but if any have been inadvertently overlooked the Publishers will be pleased to make the necessary arrangements at the first opportunity.

Hachette UK's policy is to use papers that are natural, renewable and recyclable products and made from wood grown in sustainable forests. The logging and manufacturing processes are expected to conform to the environmental regulations of the country of origin.

Orders: please contact Bookpoint Ltd, 130 Milton Park, Abingdon, Oxon OX14 4SB. Telephone: (44) 01235 827720. Fax: (44) 01235 400454. Lines are open from 9.00-5.00, Monday to Saturday, with a 24-hour message answering service. Visit our website at www.hoddereducation.co.uk

Cover photo © Andrew Brookes/CORBIS
Typeset in Bembo 12/14pt by Pantek Arts Ltd, Maidstone, Kent
Printed and bound by CPI Group (UK) Ltd, Croydon, CR0 4YY

A catalogue record for this title is available from the British Library

ISBN 978 0719 579 028

Contents

Contents

Introduction

Structure of the book

This text has primarily been written to support students in the study of Chemistry to IGCSE. The 14 topics of the examination syllabus have been divided into 25 topics to make the text more user-friendly.

The syllabus has two components, the Core and the Supplement. The Supplement defines the extended curriculum. The Core is graded C to G whereas the extended curriculum can be graded A* to G. To differentiate between these components, sections of this book covering the Supplement are shaded grey. Wherever possible this practice has also been extended to the questions, although this is not always straightforward as many questions involve material from both Core and Supplement.

Each topic starts with a list of **Key objectives**, which specify the skills and knowledge you will need to have acquired during your study of this topic. The list can also serve as a checklist of your progress with this topic.

If a particular topic includes a number of essential terms, these are defined in a table of **Key definitions**. Not all of the topics include this.

All topics have a section covering the **Key ideas**, and it is essential that you both learn and understand these sections. This is the chemistry that you will need for the IGCSE examination.

In each topic there are questions. **Sample questions** have the answers given, sometimes as model answers, while others have been answered by an imaginary student to illustrate how answers of different quality would be awarded marks. There are a few questions that you are invited to mark. If the model answer is not given with the question then it will be at the back of the book, in the **Answers**. The heading **Try this** indicates questions either from IGCSE papers or in the style of IGCSE questions. You should use these for practice and to assess your understanding and recall of the topic. All the answers and marking guidelines can be found at the back of the book.

Preparing for the examination is primarily directed at those taking the external IGCSE examination, but much of the advice offered is also relevant to internal examinations.

How to use this book

The book is complete; it contains all that is necessary to support the attainment of the highest grade. It can be used for any one or any combination of the following:

- as a textbook throughout the course
- at the end of each topic to provide reinforcement and assessment
- to prepare for internal examinations
- to prepare for the IGCSE examination.

If you want to get the maximum value from this book, it is strongly advised that you attempt to answer all the questions on paper and not in the book. Then you can repeat the exercises at intervals throughout the course.

I hope that you find this book a useful resource in your study of IGCSE Chemistry and that it assists you in gaining a commendable grade.

Bob Berry

TOPIC 1 The particulate nature of matter

Key objectives

- To know that all matter is made up of moving particles – atoms, ions or molecules
- To be able to describe the three states of matter and to explain changes of state using the kinetic theory
- To know that as the temperature increases so does the kinetic energy of the particles, that is, they move faster
- To be able to define diffusion and be able to explain this process in terms of the movement of particles
- To realise that diffusion is evidence for the movement of particles
- To know qualitatively how the rate of diffusion depends on molecular mass

Key ideas

The states of matter

	Solid	Liquid	Gas
Description	Fixed volume, own shape	Fixed volume, takes shape of container	Any volume, takes shape of container
Arrangement of particles	In a regular pattern called a lattice	Random	Random
Separation of particles	Close together, touching	Still close together, just slightly further apart than in the solid phase	Separated, far apart
Movement of particles	Vibration about a fixed position	Slow movement in a random way from place to place, sliding past each other	Fast random movement
Attractive forces between particles	Stronger than in the liquid phase	Slightly weaker than in the solid phase	No attractive forces between particles

> **Examiner's tips**
> ► Do not think that the liquid phase is half way between solid and gas. It is much closer in terms of particle arrangement to the solid phase.
> ► The interparticle forces in the solid phase are slightly *stronger* than in the liquid phase, but that does not mean that they are necessarily strong.
> ► Always make it clear that you are discussing attractive forces *between* particles, not within particles.

Changes of state

When the temperature of a solid increases, so does the energy of the particles. At the melting point, the particles have enough energy to move past each other and change positions. The lattice disappears and the particles have freedom to change positions. The liquid, unlike the solid, can flow and change its shape.

Similarly, when a liquid is heated, the energy of the particles increases. At the boiling point, the intermolecular forces can no longer hold the particles together, so the particles separate and become a vapour or gas. The particles can change position and move apart, hence gases can flow and expand to fill any space.

$$\text{solid} \underset{\underset{\substack{\text{energy given} \\ \text{to surroundings}}}{\text{cool}}}{\overset{\overset{\substack{\text{supply energy} \\ \text{heat}}}{}}{\rightleftharpoons}} \text{liquid} \underset{\underset{\substack{\text{energy given} \\ \text{to surroundings}}}{\text{cool}}}{\overset{\overset{\substack{\text{supply energy} \\ \text{heat}}}{}}{\rightleftharpoons}} \text{gas}$$

Diffusion

In both the liquid and the gaseous states, the particles have random translational motion, that is, movement from place to place. The particles will spread out to occupy the total available space (Figures 1.1a–d) – this is called diffusion.

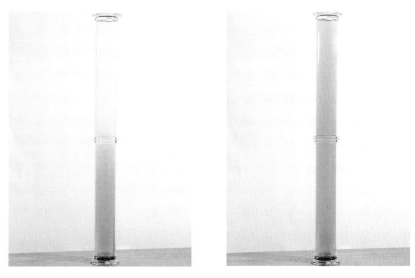

Figure 1.1a, b Diffusion of bromine gas: after 24 hours the bromine fumes have diffused throughout both jars

Figure 1.1c, d Diffusion within nickel(II) sulphate solution: diffusion throughout the liquid can take days

The kinetic theory, based on the idea of particles moving, is the only way of explaining the process of diffusion.

Rates of diffusion

- Diffusion does not occur in solids. The particles can only vibrate; they cannot move past each other or spread apart.
- Diffusion in liquids is much slower than in gases, because the particles move much more slowly in the liquid phase than in the gas phase.
- The rate at which a gas diffuses depends on its relative molecular mass. Lighter molecules move faster and will diffuse faster than heavier molecules.

Sample questions and answers

Sample question 1   Explain why the pressure of a gas in a sealed container increases when its temperature is increased.   [3 marks]

Student's answer   When the gas is heated the particles have more energy. ✓ They hit the walls of the container more frequently ✓ and harder. ✓

Examiner's comments   *The student has produced a model answer. For any GCSE marking scheme this explanation would be awarded all 3 marks.*

Sample question 2   Which gas, carbon dioxide or nitrogen, would diffuse faster? Give a reason for your answer.   [3 marks]

Students' answers   Three answers were given by different students:

Nitrogen, ✓ because it has the smaller molecules.

Nitrogen, ✓ because it is the lighter gas. ✓

Nitrogen, ✓ M_r = 28, has lighter molecules ✓ ✓ than carbon dioxide, M_r = 44. Nitrogen will diffuse faster.

Examiner's comments   *The first answer illustrates a very common error. Diffusion is often described in a question as occurring through small holes, for example in a piece of metal foil. Students imagine the hole acting as a sieve and the smaller molecules getting through the hole more easily. This is completely wrong. Another error is in thinking that smaller molecules are necessarily lighter in mass. This is not always true.*

The second response is better. If instead of 'lighter' the answer had referred to the density of the gas then 3 marks would have been awarded.

The third response is an example of a model answer, which should refer to one of the following:

- *the density of the gas*
- *the relative molecular mass, M_r*
- *the mass of one mole*
- *the mass of a molecule*
- *the speed of the molecules.*

Sample question 3   Describe the movement and arrangement of the particles in a typical solid.   [3 marks]

Student's answer   The particles are arranged and held together by strong attractive forces. The particles move back and forth.

Examiner's comments   *Read through the **Key ideas** then mark this answer yourself, with a maximum of 3 marks. The marked question with comments is on p. 118.*

Sample question 4   Explain, using the ideas of the kinetic theory, why ice is a crystalline solid with a low melting point.   [3 marks]

Examiner's comments   *This question has been included to show that the chemistry in Topic 1 can be used in other topics, particularly **Bonding: the structure of matter** (Topic 4).*

Model answer   It is crystalline because the molecules are arranged in a regular pattern called a lattice. ✓ It has a low melting point because the attractive forces between molecules ✓ are weak. ✓

Typical questions

Most typical questions follow the pattern in the sample questions above. They require descriptions of order, separation, forces and movement of particles that accompany a change; for example, a solid has melted, a liquid has boiled or a gas has been compressed.

> One common type of question asks you to predict which gas would diffuse the faster and to explain why. Or, similarly, to explain why the concentration of a gas in a mixture of gases changes. For example:
>
> A balloon contains a mixture of methane and hydrogen. After several hours the percentage of methane in the balloon has increased. Can you explain why?
>
> The correct explanation involves the relative rates of diffusion. Hydrogen, which has the lower M_r, will diffuse out of the balloon faster than methane diffuses out. The percentage of hydrogen in the balloon will decrease and the percentage of methane will increase.

TOPIC 2 Experimental techniques

Key objectives

- To be able to name the appropriate apparatus for the measurement of time, mass, temperature and volume
- To understand the concept of a pure substance
- To be aware of the importance of purity of substances in everyday life
- To know the common methods of purification
- To be able to suggest a suitable purification technique given information about the substances involved
- To be able to describe chromatography and to interpret simple chromatograms
- To be able to explain why some chromatograms have to be exposed to locating agents

Key definitions

Pure substance	A single substance
Melting point	The temperature at which a solid changes into a liquid
Boiling point	The temperature at which a liquid changes into a vapour at a certain pressure
Volatile	A volatile compound easily changes into a vapour. It has a low boiling point
Solution	A mixture of a solute, usually a solid, dissolved in the solvent, a liquid
Locating agent	A substance that reacts with colourless spots on a chromatogram and makes them visible as coloured spots

Key ideas

Importance of purification

It is important that substances used in the food, pharmaceutical and chemical industries are pure. This is necessary to ensure the safety of the consumers.

Pure and impure substances

Test	Pure substance	Impure substance
Melting point of a solid	Sharp	Melts over a temperature range and at a lower temperature than the pure solid
Boiling point of a liquid (if the impurity is a dissolved solid)	Sharp, all the liquid boils at same temperature	Boils over a temperature range and at a higher temperature than the pure liquid
Boiling point of a liquid (if the impurity is another liquid)	Sharp, all the liquid boils at same temperature	Boils over a temperature range – starts to boil at the boiling point of one liquid and rises to the boiling point of the other
Chromatography	Usually produces only one spot on the chromatogram	Produces more than one spot

Techniques for purification and for separating mixtures

Method	Used to separate or purify	Example
Filtration or centrifuging or decanting	An insoluble solid from a liquid	Sand from sea water
Simple distillation	A volatile liquid from a solution with a non-volatile solid	Pure water from aqueous copper sulphate (Water is volatile: it boils and forms a vapour; copper sulphate is non-volatile)
Fractional distillation	Liquids with different boiling points (The liquids have to be miscible, e.g. water and ethanol; water and petrol are not miscible: petrol floats as a separate layer on the water)	It can separate water and ethanol, liquid oxygen and nitrogen, and different petroleum fractions. These all form one liquid phase; they can mix. It cannot separate water and petrol, which do not mix
Evaporation	Crystals of a solute from a solution	Salt from sea water
Crystallisation	Two soluble solids if they have different solubilities in water (Dissolve in the minimum amount of hot water and cool; the less soluble salt will crystallise first)	Potassium chloride and potassium sulphate

Sample question and answer

Sample question 1 Suggest the best method to separate each of the following mixtures:
  i)   ethanol and methanol
  ii)   water from aqueous magnesium sulphate
  iii) chalk from a mixture of chalk and water
  iv)   methane and ethane
  v)   potassium chloride from aqueous potassium chloride
  vi)   a mixture of sugars from the hydrolysis of carbohydrates
  vii) carbon dioxide and hydrogen.

[7 marks]

Model answer and examiner's comments

  i)   fractional distillation ✓ *Two liquids with different boiling points.*
  ii) simple distillation ✓ *Water which is volatile will distil off.*
  iii) filtration ✓ *Chalk will be the residue in the filter paper.*
  iv) fractional distillation or diffusion ✓ *Although these are gases at room temperature, if they are cooled they can be liquefied then distilled. Methane will diffuse faster than ethane.*
  v)   evaporation or crystallisation ✓ *Evaporate the water to leave crystals of potassium chloride.*

vi)	chromatography	✓ *Sugars and amino acids can be separated or identified by this technique.*
vii)	diffusion	✓ *Gases with different relative molecular masses.*

Examiner's tip
► Do not assume that all chemistry in a question comes from the same section of the syllabus.

● **Try this** *The answers are given on p. 118.*

1 Chromatography is a valuable technique used in medical diagnosis. Chromatogram 1 in Figure 2.1 shows the amino acids in the urine of a child who is very ill with liver disease. Chromatogram 2 shows the amino acids in the urine of the same child when fully recovered.

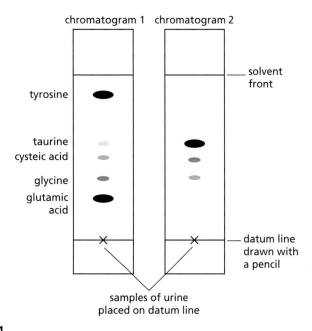

Figure 2.1

a) Amino acids are colourless compounds. How can the samples be made visible on a chromatogram?   [1 mark]

b) Why has the datum line been drawn in pencil and not in ink?
                                                              [1 mark]

c) Amino acids are identified by measuring their R_f values, where

$$R_f = \frac{\text{distance moved by amino acid}}{\text{distance moved by solvent front}}$$

Calculate the R_f value of glutamic acid using chromatogram 1.
                                                              [1 mark]

d) The R_f value of the amino acid leucine is 0.75. Where would this compound appear on chromatogram 2?   [1 mark]

e) Describe how the presence and concentration of amino acids in the urine have changed now that the child has recovered.   [3 marks]

TOPIC 3 Atomic structure and the periodic table

Key objectives

- To know the relative charges and masses of protons, electrons and neutrons
- To be able to define proton number and nucleon number
- To use these numbers to work out the numbers of protons, neutrons and electrons in an atom
- To know that the elements in the periodic table are arranged in order of increasing proton number and that similar elements are in the same group
- To be able to define the term isotope and to recall uses of radioactive isotopes in medicine and industry
- To be able to describe the arrangement of the electrons in shells for the first 20 elements
- To understand the significance of the noble gas electronic structures and valency electrons

Key definitions

Atom	The unit particle of an element
Proton number	The number of protons in one atom of the element
Nucleon number	The number of nucleons, that is, the number of protons and neutrons in one atom of the element
Element	A substance that consists of atoms all with the same proton number. It cannot be broken down into anything simpler by chemical means
Period	A horizontal row in the periodic table. It corresponds to a shell or energy level filling with electrons: the number of occupied shells is the same across the period but the number of valency electrons in the outer shell increases
Group	A vertical column in the periodic table. The number of occupied shells increases down the group but the number of valency electrons remains the same
Isotopes	Different atoms of the same element, which have the same proton number but different nucleon numbers
Noble gas	A gaseous element in Group 0, with stable electronic structure: its electron shells are full so it is unreactive

Key ideas

The atom

Particles	Relative mass	Relative charge
proton (p)	1	+1
electron (e)	1/1840	−1
neutron (n)	1	0

In an atom the number of protons and the number of electrons are equal. The atom has no overall charge: there are equal numbers of positive and negative charges.

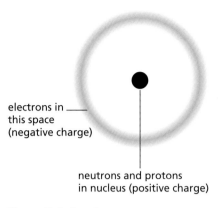

electrons in
this space
(negative charge)

neutrons and protons
in nucleus (positive charge)

Figure 3.1 An atom

The protons and neutrons, that is the nucleons, are in the central nucleus of the atom. The electrons are arranged in energy levels or shells around the nucleus (Figure 3.1).

Isotopes

Isotopes are different atoms of the same element. They have the same proton number (Z) but different nucleon numbers (A). An isotope is usually written as $^A_Z X$ where X is the symbol of the element.

Isotopes of hydrogen:

$$^1_1 H \qquad\qquad ^2_1 H \qquad\qquad ^3_1 H$$
$$1p + 1e + 0n \qquad 1p + 1e + 1n \qquad 1p + 1e + 2n$$

The different atoms of hydrogen all have one proton and one electron but the numbers of neutrons are different.

Some isotopes are radioactive. $^3_1 H$ is radioactive. The other two isotopes of hydrogen are not. The nuclei of radioactive isotopes are unstable and give off radiation.

Radioactive isotopes of uranium:

$$^{235}_{92} U \qquad\qquad ^{238}_{92} U$$
$$92p + 92e + 143n \qquad 92p + 92e + 146n$$

> **Examiner's tip**
> ▶ You must remember that, for an atom:
>
> number of protons = number of electrons = Z
> number of neutrons = number of nucleons − number of protons = $A − Z$

Uses of radioactive isotopes

Medical uses of radioisotopes include treatment of cancer, measuring the flow of fluids around the body, treatment for an overactive thyroid, location of tumours, and sterilising medical equipment.

Industrial uses include measuring and controlling thickness of paper and metal foil, measuring flow in pipelines, locating leaks, measuring engine wear, and X-raying welds.

Electronic structure of atoms

Electrons are arranged around the nucleus in energy levels or shells. The first shell is nearest to the nucleus and contains electrons with the lowest energy.

Up to calcium, $Z = 20$, the shells fill in order, 1, 2, 3, 4. The first shell can hold a maximum of two electrons; the second and third shells can each hold eight electrons. See the table overleaf.

Beyond $Z = 20$, the order of filling and the number of electrons in a shell follows a more complicated pattern.

A period in the periodic table corresponds to a shell filling, so the number of valency electrons increases across the table.

The elements in a group in the periodic table have the same number of valency electrons but an increasing number of occupied shells.

> **Examiner's tips**
> ▶ You do not have to learn the electronic structures of the first 20 elements but you must be able to work them out using a copy of the periodic table, which will be supplied for IGCSE examinations.
> ▶ You should practise writing the electronic structures of the first 20 elements using just the periodic table (at the back of this book), then check against the table given below.
> ▶ Do not be disconcerted if electronic structures that show an unfamiliar pattern are given on the question paper. For example the electron distribution of iodine is 2,8,18,18,7, and because it has 7 valency electrons its chemical properties will be similar to those of fluorine 2,7, chlorine 2,8,7 and bromine 2,8,18,7.

Electronic structures of the first 20 elements

Element	Symbol	Proton number	Energy level 1	Energy level 2	Energy level 3	Energy level 4	Electronic structure
Hydrogen	H	1	1				1
Helium	He	2	2				2
Lithium	Li	3	2	1			2,1
Beryllium	Be	4	2	2			2,2
Boron	B	5	2	3			2,3
Carbon	C	6	2	4			2,4
Nitrogen	N	7	2	5			2,5
Oxygen	O	8	2	6			2,6
Fluorine	F	9	2	7			2,7
Neon	Ne	10	2	8			2,8
Sodium	Na	11	2	8	1		2,8,1
Magnesium	Mg	12	2	8	2		2,8,2
Aluminium	Al	13	2	8	3		2,8,3
Silicon	Si	14	2	8	4		2,8,4
Phosphorus	P	15	2	8	5		2,8,5
Sulphur	S	16	2	8	6		2,8,6
Chlorine	Cl	17	2	8	7		2,8,7
Argon	Ar	18	2	8	8		2,8,8
Potassium	K	19	2	8	8	1	2,8,8,1
Calcium	Ca	20	2	8	8	2	2,8,8,2

Electronic structures can be represented as diagrams, as in Figure 3.2 opposite.

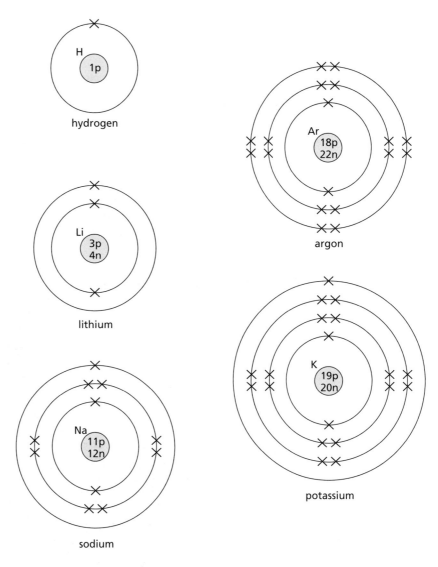

Figure 3.2 Electronic structure of hydrogen, lithium, sodium, argon and potassium

● **Try this** *You will need to refer to the periodic table of the elements (at the back of this book) to answer most of these questions. Note that for most of the elements (the most important exception being chlorine) the nucleon number approximately equals the relative atomic mass. The answers are given on p. 118.*

1   Calculate the number of protons, electrons and neutrons in one atom of the following elements:

$^{7}_{3}\text{Li}$ ....protons ....electrons ....neutrons
$^{65}_{30}\text{Zn}$ ....protons ....electrons ....neutrons
$^{108}_{47}\text{Ag}$ ....protons ....electrons ....neutrons   [3 marks]

2   What is the total number of subatomic particles in one atom of scandium?   [1 mark]

3 What is the number of charged subatomic particles in one atom of fluorine?   [1 mark]

4 Complete the electronic structures of the following. There is only ONE number missing from each structure.

   Fe   2,8,........,2
   As   2,8,18,........
   Sr   2,8,........,8,2
   Pd   2,8,18,........,2   [4 marks]

5 How many electrons are there in the outer electron shell of each of the following?

   Cs, Ra, Ge, At   [4 marks]

6 Two of the isotopes of bromine are $^{79}_{35}$Br and $^{81}_{35}$Br.
   a) What is the only difference between these two atoms?   [1 mark]
   b) Which three features are the same in both of these atoms? [3 marks]

7 Complete the following table that shows the number of protons, neutrons and electrons in different atoms. The first line has been done as an example.

Atom	Number of protons	Number of neutrons	Number of electrons
$^{19}_{9}$F	9	10	9
$^{9}_{4}$Be			
		12	11
	13	14	
		26	22
$^{127}_{53}$I			

                                                                           [12 marks]

8 Without referring to the table on p.10, write the electronic structures of the following atoms. You should use the periodic table (at the back of this book).
   i)   Li
   ii)   B
   iii) N
   iv)   Ne
   v)   Mg
   vi)   Si
   vii) S
   viii) Cl
   ix)   Ar
   x)   Ca   [10 marks]

Examiner's comments *You can check your answers using the table on p.10. If you have correctly worked out all ten electronic structures – well done. That is all that is needed for IGCSE Chemistry.*

TOPIC 4 Bonding: the structure of matter

Key objectives

- To be able to describe the differences between elements, mixtures and compounds
- To be able to describe the differences between metals and non-metals
- To know that an alloy is a mixture of a metal with another element, usually another metal
- To be able to describe the formation of ions by electron loss or gain
- To be able to describe the formation of ionic bonds between Group I and Group VII elements
- To be able to describe and explain the formation of ionic bonds between metallic and non-metallic elements
- To be able to draw and explain a simple ionic lattice
- To be able to describe the formation of single covalent bonds in simple molecules, e.g. H_2, HCl, H_2O, Cl_2 and CH_4
- To be aware of the differences in properties between ionic and covalent compounds
- To be able to draw suitable diagrams to describe the covalent bonding in more complex molecules, e.g. C_2H_4, N_2, CH_3OH and CO_2
- To know about the macromolecules diamond and graphite, their structures, properties and uses
- To be able to describe the macromolecular structure of silicon(IV) oxide and note the similarities with the structure and properties of diamond
- To be able to describe metallic bonding and use this to explain the electrical conductivity and malleability of metals

Key ideas

Elements

An element consists of atoms all with the same proton number. It cannot be broken down into anything simpler by chemical means.

Mixtures and compounds

Mixture	Compound
A mixture contains at least two substances or different particles, not chemically bonded. Air contains oxygen and nitrogen molecules, O_2 and N_2	A compound contains atoms of two or more different elements, chemically bonded. The compound water contains hydrogen and oxygen bonded as water molecules, H_2O
A mixture can have any composition	The composition of a pure compound is fixed. Copper oxide has the composition 80% copper and 20% oxygen by mass
The formation of a mixture is a physical rather than a chemical change	The formation of a compound is a chemical change
The properties of a mixture are those of its components	The properties of a compound are its own and not those of its constituent elements. The properties of magnesium oxide are different from those of both magnesium and oxygen
The components of a mixture are not chemically bonded together, so they can be separated by physical means, e.g. distillation	Chemical reactions have to be used to separate a compound into its constituent elements

Metals and non-metals

These are discussed in Topic 15.

Formation of ions and ionic compounds

An ion is a charged atom or group of atoms. In an ion the number of protons does not equal the number of electrons.

> **Examiner's tips**
> *The following ideas are essential to understanding how and why ionic bonds form.*
> ▶ Ions are formed by atoms gaining or losing electrons so that they have the same electronic structure as the nearest noble gas.
> ▶ Metallic atoms lose electrons and form positive ions or cations.
> ▶ Non-metallic atoms gain electrons and form negative ions or anions.
> ▶ Oppositely charged ions attract each other: there is a strong electrostatic force between them called an ionic bond.
> ▶ Compounds that have ionic bonds are called ionic compounds. Examples include sodium chloride, magnesium oxide and magnesium chloride.

In the formation of sodium chloride, a sodium atom has the electronic structure 2,8,1, so the outer electron is lost to leave the sodium ion, which has the stable electronic structure 2,8. The sodium atom has 11 protons and 11 electrons and so has no charge; the sodium ion has 11 protons and 10 electrons so it has a single positive charge. The sodium ion is written as Na^+.

A chlorine atom has the electronic structure 2,8,7, so an extra electron needs to be gained to complete the outer shell. This will form the chloride ion, Cl^-, which has the stable electronic structure 2,8,8. The chlorine atom has 17 protons and 17 electrons and so has no charge; the chloride ion has 17 protons and 18 electrons so it has a single negative charge.

Ionic compounds can be represented by diagrams of the type shown in Figure 4.1.

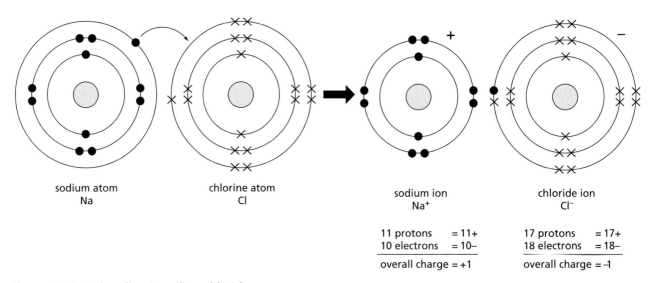

		11 protons = 11+ 10 electrons = 10–	17 protons = 17+ 18 electrons = 18–
		overall charge = +1	overall charge = –1

Figure 4.1 Ionic bonding in sodium chloride

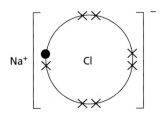

× electron from chlorine atom
● electron from sodium atom

Figure 4.2 Ionic bonding in sodium chloride, simplified

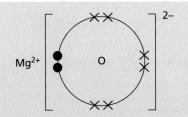

Figure 4.3 Magnesium oxide

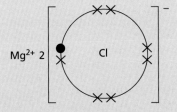

Figure 4.4 Magnesium chloride

Alternatively, a simpler type of diagram can be used that only shows the valency electrons. Although both representations are correct, the simpler type of diagram shown in Figure 4.2 is preferred at IGCSE.

The ionic diagram for magnesium oxide is shown in Figure 4.3. The reason for the 2+ and 2− is that two electrons are lost by the magnesium atom and two are gained by the oxygen atom.

Mg 2,8,2   becomes Mg^{2+} 2,8
12p and 12e   12p and 10e = 2+

O   becomes O^{2-}
8p and 8e   8p and 10e = 2−

In magnesium chloride, Figure 4.4, the ionic bonding is different. A magnesium atom will lose two electrons and a chlorine atom will gain one electron. One magnesium ion Mg^{2+} will therefore combine with two chloride ions Cl^-.

Ionic structures

The lattice structure in a crystal of an ionic compound, such as sodium chloride, is a regular three-dimensional arrangement of alternating positive and negative ions (Figure 4.5). It is held together by strong electrostatic forces. There are no molecules, just ions.

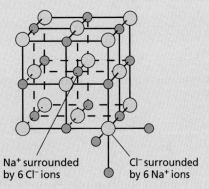

Na^+ surrounded by 6 Cl^- ions Cl^- surrounded by 6 Na^+ ions

Figure 4.5 Ionic structure of sodium chloride

● **Try this** *The answers are given on p. 118.*

1 Use the periodic table to predict the charge on an ion of each of the following.

    I, Cs, Se, Ba, P   [5 marks]

2 State how many protons, electrons and neutrons there are in the following ions.
   i) $^{9}_{4}Be^{2+}$ ....protons ....electrons ....neutrons
   ii) $^{55}_{25}Mn^{2+}$ ....protons ....electrons ....neutrons
   iii) $^{70}_{31}Ga^{3+}$ ....protons ....electrons ....neutrons
   iv) $^{75}_{33}As^{3-}$ ....protons ....electrons ....neutrons
   v) $^{80}_{35}Br^{-}$ ....protons ....electrons ....neutrons   [5 marks]

3 Draw a diagram to show the arrangement of the valency electrons in the following ionic compounds.
   i)   potassium fluoride   [2 marks]
   ii) calcium sulphide   [2 marks]
   iii) lithium oxide   [3 marks]
   iv) aluminium fluoride   [3 marks]

Covalent bonding

Atoms can attain the stable noble gas electronic structure by sharing electrons. A pair of electrons, one from each atom, may be shared. This is a single covalent bond and it holds the two atoms together. They form a molecule.

Covalent bonds form between non-metals in which both atoms need one or more electrons to achieve a noble gas electronic structure.

The hydrogen molecule H_2 is an example of covalent bonding (Figure 4.6). The single covalent bond can be represented by a line:

    H—H

By sharing an electron pair, both hydrogen atoms have two electrons in their outer electron shell, the same as the noble gas helium.

shared electrons

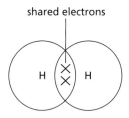

Figure 4.6 Covalent bonding in the hydrogen molecule

Other covalent molecules

● **Chlorine, Cl$_2$** The electronic structure of a chlorine atom is 2,8,7. The two atoms each contribute one electron to the bond, so each chlorine atom then has six electrons and the shared pair, giving eight electrons in the outer shell (Figure 4.7).

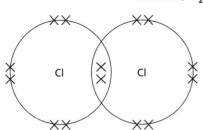

Figure 4.7 The chlorine molecule

● **Hydrogen chloride, HCl** The electronic structures of the atoms are H 1 and Cl 2,8,7. Both atoms need to gain one electron. They both have a valency of one and form one covalent bond per atom (Figure 4.8).

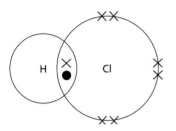

Figure 4.8 The hydrogen chloride molecule

● **Water, H$_2$O** The electronic structures of the atoms are H 1 and O 2,6. Hydrogen needs to gain one electron, so it can form one bond per atom. Oxygen needs to gain two electrons per atom, so it has a valency of two and will form two bonds per atom (Figure 4.9).

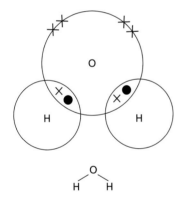

Figure 4.9 The water molecule

● **Methane, CH$_4$** The electronic structures of the atoms are H 1 and C 2,4. The valency of carbon is four, so four hydrogen atoms will bond to one carbon atom (Figure 4.10).

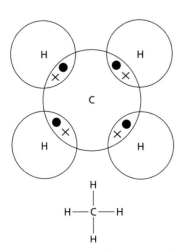

Figure 4.10 The methane molecule

More complex covalent molecules

Nitrogen, N_2

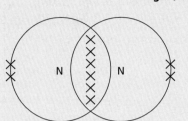

Figure 4.11 Covalent bonding in the nitrogen molecule

The electronic structure of a nitrogen atom is 2,5. Each atom needs to gain three electrons, its valency is three and it will form three bonds per atom (Figure 4.11). Six electrons, that is three pairs, are shared. This is a triple bond.

Carbon dioxide, CO_2

Between the carbon atom and each oxygen atom four electrons, that is two pairs, are shared (Figure 4.12). This is a double bond, represented by two lines. Carbon with a valency of four has formed four bonds per atom, whereas oxygen has formed two bonds per atom.

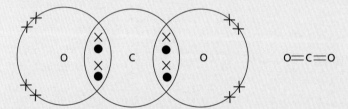

Figure 4.12 The carbon dioxide molecule

Ethene, C_2H_4   The bonding in ethene is shown in Figure 4.13.

Methanol, CH_3OH   The bonding in the methanol is shown in Figure 4.14.

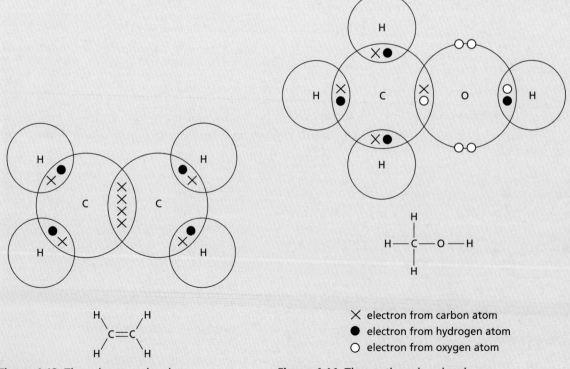

X electron from carbon atom
● electron from hydrogen atom
○ electron from oxygen atom

Figure 4.13 The ethene molecule

Figure 4.14 The methanol molecule

Differences between ionic and covalent compounds

Property	Ionic compounds	Covalent compounds
Elements in compound	Metal and non-metal	Two or more non-metals
Type of particle	Only ions	Simple molecules
Volatility –melting point and boiling point	High melting and boiling points because ions are held together by strong forces	Low melting and boiling points because intermolecular forces are weak
Solubility	Most are soluble in water but insoluble in organic solvents	Most are insoluble in water but soluble in organic solvents
Electrical conductivity	Conduct when molten or dissolved in water because the ions are free to move. Do not conduct as solids, because the ions cannot move to the electrodes	In general do not conduct as solids, liquids or in solution, because there are no ions, only molecules. A few react with water and form ions, and these will conduct in aqueous solution, for example hydrogen chloride

Macromolecules

These are giant covalent structures which have millions of atoms held together by covalent bonds. Examples of macromolecular substances are diamond, graphite and silicon(IV) oxide.

● **Diamond**   This is a crystalline form of the element carbon. It has a three-dimensional structure in which every carbon atom is covalently bonded to four other carbon atoms (Figure 4.15).

Properties of diamond	Uses
Very high melting point	
Hardest substance known	Drill bits; cutting glass and metals
Does not conduct electricity	
Colourless crystals that glitter	Jewellery

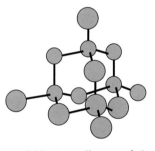

Figure 4.15 A small part of the structure of diamond

● **Graphite**   This is another form of the element carbon. The atoms are covalently bonded in layers, with each carbon atom strongly bonded to three other atoms in the same layer (Figure 4.16). The bonding between the layers is much weaker and the electrons responsible for these bonds are free to move within the structure. They are described as delocalised or as a 'sea of electrons'.

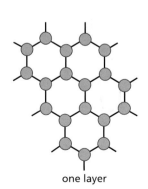
one layer

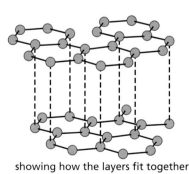
showing how the layers fit together

Figure 4.16 The structure of graphite

Properties of graphite	Uses
Black shiny solid	
Soft with a slippery almost soapy feel: the layers can slip over each other because of the weak bonds between layers	As a lubricant In pencils
Good conductor of electricity because the electrons between the layers are mobile	To make electrodes
High melting point because the strong bonds in the layers have to break before the graphite can melt	

● **Silicon(IV) oxide**

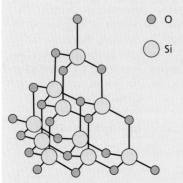

● O
○ Si

Figure 4.17 The silicon(IV) oxide structure in quartz

This is a compound: it contains two elements.

Si 2,8,4   Silicon forms four bonds per atom.
O 2,6   Oxygen forms two bonds per atom.

One silicon atom is bonded to four oxygen atoms; each oxygen atom is bonded to two silicon atoms (Figure 4.17). Its structure is very similar to that of diamond, consequently its properties are very similar. Silicon(IV) oxide in the form of quartz exists as clear colourless crystals. They are very hard, have a high melting point and do not conduct electricity.

● **Try this** *The answers are given on p. 119.*

4 Predict the valency, that is, the number of covalent bonds per atom, of the following elements.

   i) bromine

   ii) arsenic

   iii) germanium

   iv) tellurium

   v) phosphorus   [5 marks]

Examiner's tip

▶ Writing the formulae of compounds is a very important skill and needs to be practised. Use the periodic table to find the symbols of the elements and their valencies. Then follow this example for silicon sulphide:

symbol	Si	S
valency	4	2

Now 'swap' the numbers: Si_2S_4
Where possible, cancel: Si_1S_2
which is written as SiS_2
There is more practice on this in Topic 5.

5 Write the formula for each of the following covalent compounds.

   i) hydrogen fluoride

   ii) nitrogen chloride

   iii) germanium oxide

   iv) phosphorus nitride

   v) oxygen fluoride   [5 marks]

6 For each of the following, draw a diagram showing the arrangement of the valency electrons in one molecule of the covalent compound.

   i) ammonia NH_3 [2 marks]

   ii) silicon hydride   [3 marks]

   iii) oxygen molecule O_2 [2 marks]

   iv) phosphorus fluoride   [3 marks]

   v) hydrogen sulphide   [3 marks]

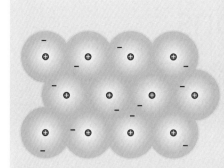

Figure 4.18 One layer in the structure of a metal

Metallic bonding

The structure of a metal can be described as a lattice of positive ions in a 'sea of electrons' (Figure 4.18). These electrons are described as free, mobile or delocalised; they can move throughout the metal. The strong attractive force between the positive ions and the negatively charged electrons is the metallic bond. Remember: a positive and a negative charge attract.

Common error

The positive particles are positive ions, that is, cations. The atoms have lost their valency electrons, for example Na^+ and Cu^{2+}. It is a very common mistake is to think that the lattice consists of protons or atomic nuclei rather than cations. ■

● **Properties of metals**

Metals are malleable, which means when hammered they change shape and do not break. The bond between the layers may be strong but it is non-directional. The layers can slip over each other, so that the piece of metal has a new shape and new bonds form (Figure 4.19).

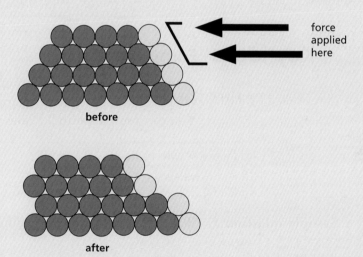

force applied here

before

after

Figure 4.19 The positions of the positive ions in a metal before and after a force has been applied

Metals are good conductors of electricity. When a voltage is applied across a piece of metal, the delocalised electrons move to the positive end and a current flows through the metal.

21 ●

TOPIC 5 Stoichiometry: formulae and equations

Key objectives
- To be able to write the formulae of simple compounds
- To deduce the formula of a simple compound from the relative numbers of atoms present
- To deduce the formula of a simple compound from a model or a diagrammatic representation
- To determine the formula of an ionic compound from the charges on the ions
- To be able to construct word equations and simple balanced chemical equations
- To be able to construct equations with state symbols
- To be able to write ionic equations
- To deduce the balanced equation for a chemical reaction given relevant information

Examiner's tip
▶ The objectives regarding writing equations are long term. You should develop, practise and reinforce these skills throughout your IGCSE Chemistry course.

Key ideas Formulae

To write the formula of a compound, you need to know the valencies of the elements or structural groups in that compound. You can use the periodic table to find valencies.

Group	I	II	III	IV	V	VI	VII	0
Valency	1	2	3	4	3	2	1	0

Sample question 1   Write the formula of aluminium oxide.   [1 mark]

Model answer   symbol   Al   O

valency   3   2

'Swap' the numbers and, if possible, cancel.

The formula for aluminium oxide is Al_2O_3. ✓

Sample question 2   Write the formula of aluminium phosphide.   [1 mark]

Model answer   symbol   Al   P

valency   3   3

Al_3P_3, cancel numbers: Al_1P_1, written as AlP. ✓

You cannot predict the valencies of the transition elements from the periodic table.

Also, you will have to learn the valencies of some of the common structural groups:

hydroxide	OH	valency	1
nitrate	NO_3	valency	1
carbonate	CO_3	valency	2
sulphate	SO_4	valency	2

You can write formulae of their compounds by balancing the charges on the ions. For example:

aluminium sulphate $\quad Al^{3+} \times 2 = 6+ \quad SO_4^{2-} \times 3 = 6-$

The formula is $Al_2(SO_4)_3$. Brackets are used because there is more than one element in the sulphate group, all to be multiplied by 3.

● **Try this** *The answers are given on p. 119.*

1 Write the formula of the following simple compounds.
   i) lithium iodide
   ii) sodium oxide
   iii) boron fluoride
   iv) calcium nitride
   v) germanium chloride
   vi) arsenic oxide
   vii) aluminium sulphide
   viii) silicon carbide [8 marks]

2 Work out the formula of the following compounds from the ions present.
   i) sodium sulphate: Na^+ and SO_4^{2-}
   ii) aluminium hydroxide: Al^{3+} and OH^-
   iii) calcium nitrate: Ca^{2+} and NO_3^-
   iv) magnesium carbonate: Mg^{2+} and CO_3^{2-}
   v) calcium phosphate: Ca^{2+} and PO_4^{3-} [5 marks]

3 Work out the formula of each compound from the diagram of its structure, in Figure 5.1.

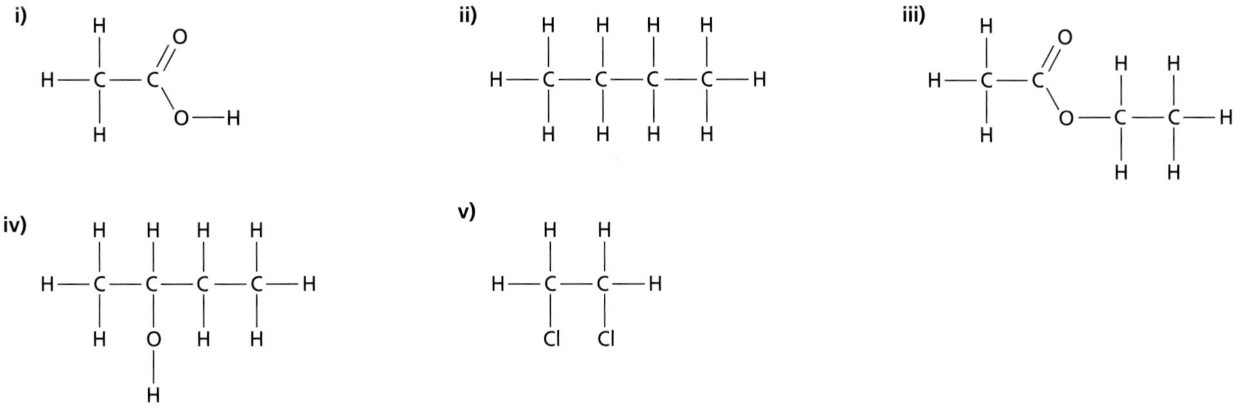

Figure 5.1

Writing equations

This skill will be introduced in this topic and developed throughout the course. All chemical reactions can be represented by equations. The easiest type of equation is a word equation.

$$\text{magnesium} + \text{oxygen} \rightarrow \text{magnesium oxide}$$

reactants   product

The most widely used type of equation is the symbol equation. This has to balance, that is, there needs to be the same number of each type of atom on both sides of the equation.

For all metals, simply write the symbol in an equation. Some non-metals exist as diatomic molecules (two atoms per molecule), for example O_2, N_2, H_2, Cl_2. Other non-metals are written as the atom, for example C, Si, B, P, S.

$$Mg + O_2 \rightarrow MgO$$

The above equation does not balance.

1Mg   1Mg
2O   1O

Common error

You must not alter any of the symbols or formulae. The following is wrong.

$$Mg + O_2 \rightarrow MgO_2$$

You must not change the formula of magnesium oxide from the correct one, MgO, to an incorrect one, MgO_2, in an attempt to balance the equation. ■

Numbers need to be written in front of a reactant and/or product to balance the equation.

$$2Mg + O_2 \rightarrow 2MgO$$

reactants   product
2Mg   2Mg
2O   2O

Both sides are equal – the equation balances.

State symbols

The state symbols are:

(s)   solid
(l)   liquid
(g)   gas
(aq)   aqueous, that is, dissolved in water

These follow the symbols or formulae in equations, for example:

$$2Mg(s) + O_2(g) \rightarrow 2MgO(s)$$

A more complex example

Word equation:

$$\text{aluminium hydroxide} + \text{hydrochloric acid} \rightarrow \text{aluminium chloride} + \text{water}$$

Symbol equation:

$$Al(OH)_3 + HCl \rightarrow AlCl_3 + H_2O \qquad \text{unbalanced}$$

$$Al(OH)_3 + 3HCl \rightarrow AlCl_3 + 3H_2O \qquad \text{balanced}$$

$$Al(OH)_3(s) + 3HCl(aq) \rightarrow AlCl_3(aq) + 3H_2O(l)$$
$$\text{with state symbols}$$

● **Try this** *This is an opportunity for you to practise writing some simple equations. More complex examples will be introduced later in the course. The answers are given on p. 120.*

4 Balance the following equations. You must not alter any of the symbols or formulae.

i) $Na + Cl_2 \rightarrow NaCl$

ii) $Ca + O_2 \rightarrow CaO$

iii) $Fe + Br_2 \rightarrow FeBr_3$

iv) $Li + O_2 \rightarrow Li_2O$

v) $P + O_2 \rightarrow P_2O_3$

vi) $MgO + HCl \rightarrow MgCl_2 + H_2O$

vii) $Na + H_2O \rightarrow NaOH + H_2$

viii) $FeCl_3 + NaOH \rightarrow Fe(OH)_3 + NaCl$ [8 marks]

5 Write balanced symbol equations for the following reactions. You will find it helpful to refer to the equations in question 4.

i) potassium + bromine $\rightarrow$ potassium bromide

ii) aluminium + iodine $\rightarrow$ aluminium iodide

iii) sodium + oxygen $\rightarrow$ sodium oxide

iv) magnesium chloride + sodium hydroxide $\rightarrow$ magnesium hydroxide + sodium chloride

v) calcium + hydrochloric acid (HCl) $\rightarrow$ calcium chloride + hydrogen [10 marks]

TOPIC 6 Stoichiometry: calculations

Key objectives

- To be able to define the terms relative atomic mass, relative formula mass, mole and the Avogadro constant
- To be able to calculate reacting masses using simple proportions
- To be able to calculate reacting masses and volumes of gases and solutions using the mole concept
- To understand the idea of a limiting reagent
- To be able to calculate empirical and molecular formulae
- To be able to calculate % yield and % purity

Key definitions

Relative atomic mass (A_r) The average mass of the naturally occurring atoms on a scale where an atom of ^{12}C has a mass = 12.000 (Most naturally occurring elements are a mixture of isotopes. This means that not all the atoms have the same mass so the average has to be used.)

Relative formula mass (M_r) The sum of the relative atomic masses of all the elements shown in the formula (For substances that consist of simple molecules the term relative molecular mass (M_r) can be used instead of relative formula mass.)

Mole The amount of a substance that contains 6×10^{23} atoms, ions or molecules. The number 6×10^{23} is called the Avogadro constant. One mole of a substance has a mass equal to the relative formula mass in grams

Empirical formula This shows the simplest ratio of atoms present

Molecular formula This shows the number of atoms of each element present in one molecule of the substance

Molar volume (V_m) The volume, approximately 24 dm³, occupied by one mole of any gas at room temperature and pressure (r.t.p.)

Concentration of a solution Measure of the amount of solute in unit volume of solution; units mol/dm³ or g/dm³

Examiner's tips

If you learn these useful relationships you are more likely to be successful in performing chemical calculations.

▶ Number of moles $= \dfrac{\text{mass of substance}}{\text{mass of one mole}}$

▶ Number of moles of a gas $= \dfrac{\text{volume of gas in dm}^3 \text{ at r.t.p.}}{24}$

▶ $\begin{array}{l}\text{Number of moles} \\ \text{of solute}\end{array} = \begin{array}{c}\text{concentration of solution} \\ \text{(mol/dm}^3)\end{array} \times \begin{array}{c}\text{volume of solution} \\ \text{(dm}^3)\end{array}$

Examples Relative formula masses and moles

You can find the relative atomic masses using the periodic table (at the back of this book).

Sample question 1   Calculate the relative formula mass of the following.
i) CH_4
ii) $Ca(OH)_2$
iii) $Al_2(SO_4)_3$ [3 marks]

Model answers   i) CH_4 $(1 \times 12) + (4 \times 1) = 16$ ✓
ii) $Ca(OH)_2$ $(1 \times 40) + 2(16 + 1) = 74$ ✓
iii) $Al_2(SO_4)_3$ $(2 \times 27) + 3(32 + 4 \times 16) = 54 + (3 \times 96) = 342$ ✓

> **Examiner's tip**
> ▶ If the formula involves a group in brackets, it is easier to work out the formula mass inside the bracket first and then multiply by the number outside the brackets.

● **Try this**   *The answers are given on p. 120.*

1   Calculate the relative formula mass of the following.
i) C_2H_6
ii) Na_2CO_3
iii) Al_2O_3
iv) $C_4H_{10}O$
v) $Al(OH)_3$ [5 marks]

2   Calculate the mass of one mole of the following.
i) H_2O
ii) C_3H_8
iii) NaOH
iv) $MgCO_3$
v) $CuSO_4.5H_2O$ [5 marks]

> **Examiner's tip**
> ▶ In question 2 v) the 5 multiplies H_2O only.

3   What is the mass of each of the following?
i) 2 moles of H_2O
ii) 3 moles of C_2H_4
iii) 0.5 moles of NaOH
iv) 0.125 moles of MgO
v) 0.7 moles of SO_3 [10 marks]

> **Examiner's tip**
> ▶ Rearrange the relationship
>
> $$\text{number of moles} = \frac{\text{mass of substance}}{\text{mass of one mole}}$$
>
> to give
>
> $$\text{mass of substance} = \text{number of moles} \times \text{mass of one mole}$$
>
> You will need to calculate the mass of one mole of the substance first.

Reacting masses

These questions are concerned with reacting masses, i.e. how much reacts or is formed. There are two methods of performing this type of calculation – one does not involve moles, the other method does. Both methods are used to answer the sample question.

Sample question 2 Calculate the mass of magnesium oxide formed when 3.0 g of magnesium reacts with excess oxygen. [3 marks]

> **Examiner's tip**
> ▶ The reaction will stop when all the magnesium is used up; it is the limiting reagent. When all the magnesium has reacted, some oxygen will be remain, as the question states – it is in excess.

Model answers *Method 1*

$$2Mg + O_2 \rightarrow 2MgO \quad M_r \text{ of MgO} = 24 + 16 = 40$$
$$2 \times 24 \qquad 2 \times 40$$

48 g of magnesium will form 80 g of magnesium oxide ✓

1 g of magnesium will form $\dfrac{80}{48}$ g of magnesium oxide

3 g of magnesium will form $\dfrac{80}{48} \times 3$ g of magnesium oxide ✓

$= 5.0$ g ✓

Method 2

$$2Mg + O_2 \rightarrow 2MgO \quad M_r \text{ of MgO} = 24 + 16 = 40$$

Number of moles of Mg $= \dfrac{3}{24} = 0.125$ ✓

Mole ratio Mg : MgO $= 2 : 2 = 1 : 1$

Moles of MgO formed $= 0.125$ ✓

Mass of magnesium oxide $= 0.125 \times 40 = 5.0$ g ✓

> **Examiner's tip**
> ▶ You only use the numbers that balance the equation in the mole ratio. You must ignore them when working out the mass of a mole of Mg or MgO. You can expect to be given the equation in the question.

● **Try this** *You can use method 1 or method 2. The answers are given on p. 120.*

4   Calculate the mass of oxygen needed to burn 20 g of methane.

$$CH_4 + 2O_2 \rightarrow CO_2 + 2H_2O$$ [3 marks]

5   Calculate the mass of copper(II) sulphate formed when 5.0 g of copper(II) oxide reacts with excess sulphuric acid.

$$CuO + H_2SO_4 \rightarrow CuSO_4 + H_2O$$ [3 marks]

Moles and volumes of gases

The method is essentially the same as for reacting masses. Use $V_m = 24\ dm^3$ for one mole of any gas at room temperature and pressure (r.t.p.).

● **Try this** *The answers are given on p. 120.*

6 Calculate the number of moles of oxygen molecules, O_2, in the following volumes of oxygen gas at r.t.p.
   i) $48\ dm^3$
   ii) $1.2\ dm^3$
   iii) $960\ dm^3$
   iv) $3.6\ dm^3$
   v) $1200\ cm^3$ (Remember $1\ dm^3 = 1000\ cm^3$)   [5 marks]

Examiner's tip
▶ Work out the number of moles of O_2 then use $V_m = 24\ dm^3$ at r.t.p. to find the volume.

7 Calculate the volume of oxygen at r.t.p. for each of the following masses of the gas.
   i) $1.6\ g$
   ii) $320\ g$
   iii) $4.8\ g$
   iv) $8\ g$
   v) $40\ g$ [10 marks]

Reacting volumes

Sample question 3   Calculate the volume of oxygen at r.t.p. necessary to burn $1.4\ g$ of butene.   [4 marks]

Model answer $C_4H_8 + 6O_2 \rightarrow 4CO_2 + 4H_2O$

M_r of butene $= (4 \times 12) + (8 \times 1) = 56$ ✓

Moles of $C_4H_8 = \dfrac{1.4}{56} = 0.025$ ✓

Mole ratio $C_4H_8 : O_2 = 1 : 6$

Moles of oxygen reacted $= 0.025 \times 6 = 0.15$ ✓

Volume of oxygen at r.t.p. $= 0.15 \times 24 = 3.6\ dm^3$ ✓

● **Try this** *The answers are given on p. 120.*

8 What volume of carbon dioxide is produced by the reaction described in Sample question 3, that is when $1.4\ g$ of butene is burnt in oxygen?   [3 marks]

Examiner's tip
▶ In question 9, just look at the equation. There is no need to use $V_m = 24\ dm^3$.

9 What is the volume of oxygen needed to react with $20\ cm^3$ of ethane?
   $2C_2H_6 + 7O_2 \rightarrow 4CO_2 + 6H_2O$ [2 marks]

10 Calculate the volume of sulphur trioxide formed when $20.0\ g$ of iron(III) sulphate is heated.
   $Fe_2(SO_4)_3 \rightarrow Fe_2O_3 + 3SO_3$ [4 marks]

11   When aluminium was reacted with an excess of hydrochloric acid, 0.72 dm³ of hydrogen at r.t.p. was formed. Calculate the mass of aluminium used.

$$2Al + 6HCl \rightarrow 2AlCl_3 + 3H_2$$ [3 marks]

Empirical and molecular formulae

Sample question 4   A hydrocarbon contains 92.3% of carbon. Its relative molecular mass is 78. Calculate its empirical and molecular formulae.

[4 marks]

Examiner's tip

▶ Hydrocarbons contain only carbon and hydrogen.

Model answer

	carbon	hydrogen
Percentage composition by mass	92.3	7.7
Divide by A_r to find mole ratio carbon atoms to hydrogen atoms	$\frac{92.3}{12} = 7.69$ ✓	$\frac{7.7}{1} = 7.7$ ✓
Divide by the lowest number to find the simplest whole number ratio	1	1

The empirical formula is CH. ✓
The molecular formula has to be a multiple of the empirical formula, for example CH, C_2H_2, C_3H_3 etc.
M_r of CH = 13
M_r of the hydrocarbon = 78
$\frac{78}{13} = 6$ So the molecular formula is C_6H_6. ✓

● **Try this**   *The answers are given on p. 120.*

12   A compound contains 38.7% carbon, 9.67% hydrogen and 51.6% oxygen. Its relative molecular mass is 62. Calculate its empirical and molecular formulae.   [4 marks]

Moles and concentration of solutions

You are strongly advised not to attempt these questions until you have done some practical work involving titrations.

Examiner's tips

▶ A useful relationship is

$$\text{concentration (mol/dm}^3\text{)} = \frac{\text{number of moles}}{\text{volume of solution (dm}^3\text{)}}$$

▶ Most of the practical work and information in questions gives volumes in cm³. You will have to change from cm³ into dm³. (1 dm³ = 1000 cm³)

● **Try this**   *The answers are given on p. 120.*

13   Calculate the concentrations (in mol/dm³) of the following solutions of sodium hydroxide, NaOH. The M_r of sodium hydroxide is 40.
   i)   2 g in 100 cm³
   ii) 25 g in 500 cm³
   iii) 1 g in 10 cm³   [6 marks]

14 Calculate the mass of solute necessary to make the following solutions.

    i) 100 cm³ of potassium hydroxide, KOH, concentration 0.5 mol/dm³.

                                                                  [3 marks]

    ii) 50 cm³ of sodium carbonate, Na_2CO_3, concentration 0.1 mol/dm³.

                                                                    [3 marks]

    iii) 3 dm³ of sodium chloride, NaCl, concentration 2.5 mol/dm³.

                                                                    [3 marks]

Sample question 5 Calculate the volume of sodium hydroxide, concentration 0.16 mol/dm³, needed to neutralise 20 cm³ of sulphuric acid, concentration 0.2 mol/dm³.   **[3 marks]**

Model answer $2NaOH + H_2SO_4 \rightarrow Na_2SO_4 + 2H_2O$

Moles of $H_2SO_4 = \dfrac{20}{10000} \times 0.2 = 0.004$ ✓

Moles of NaOH $= 0.004 \times 2 = 0.008$ ✓ (*Look at the mole ratio in the equation*).

Rearrange the equation

$$\text{concentration (mol/dm}^3) = \frac{\text{number of moles}}{\text{volume of solution (dm}^3)}$$

to give

$$\text{volume} = \frac{\text{number of moles}}{\text{concentration}}$$

$$= \frac{0.008}{0.16} = 0.05\,\text{dm}^3 \text{ or } 50\,\text{cm}^3 \checkmark$$

● **Try this** *The answer is given on p. 121.*

15 25 cm³ of sodium carbonate, 0.10 mol/dm³, was neutralised by 31.0 cm³ of hydrochloric acid. Calculate the concentration of the acid in mol/dm³.

$$Na_2CO_3 + 2HCl \rightarrow 2NaCl + CO_2 + H_2O \qquad \text{[3 marks]}$$

Moles, % yield and % purity

Sample question 6 Excess magnesium carbonate was added to 25.0 cm³ of sulphuric acid, concentration 2.0 mol/dm³. The unreacted magnesium carbonate was removed by filtration. The solution of magnesium sulphate was evaporated to give 6.7 g of hydrated magnesium sulphate crystals. Calculate the percentage yield.

$$MgCO_3 + H_2SO_4 \rightarrow MgSO_4 + CO_2 + H_2O$$
$$MgSO_4 + 7H_2O \rightarrow MgSO_4.7H_2O \qquad \text{[5 marks]}$$

Model answer From the equations:

1 mole of H_2SO_4 gives 1 mole of $MgSO_4$ which gives 1 mole of $MgSO_4.7H_2O$

Number of moles of H_2SO_4 = number of moles of $MgSO_4.7H_2O$

Number of moles of $H_2SO_4 = \dfrac{25 \times 2.0}{1000} = 0.05$ ✓

Number of moles of $MgSO_4.7H_2O$ = 0.05 ✓

Mass of 1 mole of $MgSO_4.7H_2O$ = $24 + 32 + (16 \times 4) + 7 \times 18 = 246$ ✓

Theoretical yield = $0.05 \times 246 = 12.3\,g$ ✓

Percentage yield = $\dfrac{\text{actual yield} \times 100}{\text{theoretical yield}} = \dfrac{6.7 \times 100}{12.3} = 54.5\%$ ✓

● **Try this** *The answers are given on p. 121.*

16 12.0 g of ethanoic acid reacted with an excess of ethanol to form 7.2 g of ethyl ethanoate. Calculate the percentage yield.

$CH_3COOH + C_2H_5OH \rightarrow CH_3COOC_2H_5 + H_2O$ [4 marks]

17 An excess of nickel oxide reacted with 50.0 cm³ of hydrochloric acid, concentration 1.6 mol/dm³, to form 6.1 g of hydrated nickel chloride crystals. Calculate the percentage yield.

$NiO + 2HCl \rightarrow NiCl_2 + H_2O$

$NiCl_2 + 6H_2O \rightarrow NiCl_2.6H_2O$ [5 marks]

Sample question 7 7.0 g of impure calcium carbonate was heated and 2.42 g of carbon dioxide was collected. Calculate the percentage purity of the calcium carbonate.

$CaCO_3 \rightarrow CaO + CO_2$ [5 marks]

Model answer 1 mole of $CaCO_3$ formed 1 mole of CO_2

Moles of $CaCO_3$ = moles of CO_2

> **Examiner's tip**
> ▶ You must use the mass of carbon dioxide; remember the 7.0 g contains calcium carbonate and impurities.

Moles of CO_2 = $\dfrac{2.42}{44} = 0.055$ ✓

(Mass of 1 mole of CO_2 = $12 + 16 + 16 = 44$) ✓

Moles of $CaCO_3$ = 0.055

Mass of 1 mole of $CaCO_3$ = $40 + 12 + 3 \times 16 + 100$ ✓

Mass of pure calcium carbonate = $0.055 \times 100 = 5.5\,g$ ✓

Percentage purity = $\dfrac{\text{mass of pure substance}}{\text{mass of impure substance}} \times 100$

$= \dfrac{5.5 \times 100}{7.0} = 78.6\%$ ✓

Try this

This question is similar but not identical to Sample question 7. The answer is given on p. 121.

18 9.30 g of impure sodium hydrogencarbonate was heated. 2.24 g of carbon dioxide was formed. Calculate the percentage purity of the sodium hydrogencarbonate.

$$2NaHCO_3 \rightarrow Na_2CO_3 + CO_2 + H_2O$$ [5 marks]

> **Examiner's tip**
>
> ▶ If a calculation is worth more than 1 mark, you are strongly advised to show your working. In the following example on limiting reagents and reagents in excess, there is a deliberate mistake at the beginning of the calculation. This will illustrate how examiners mark such an answer and emphasise that it is still possible to be awarded marks.

Sample question 8

In this question one reactant is in excess – some of it will be left unreacted. The other reactant is the limiting reagent – it will all be used up and then the reaction will stop.

0.5 g of magnesium is added to a solution containing 3.0 g of ethanoic acid. Which is the limiting reagent and how many moles of the other reagent are left unreacted?

$$Mg + 2CH_3COOH \rightarrow (CH_3COO)_2Mg + H_2$$ [5 marks]

Student's answer

Moles of Mg = $\dfrac{0.5}{12}$ = 0.0417 ✗

M_r of CH_3COOH = 60 ✓ Moles of CH_3COOH = $\dfrac{3}{60}$ = 0.05 ✓

The limiting reagent is ethanoic acid, ✓ because 0.05 moles of ethanoic acid can only react with 0.025 moles of Mg.

(Look at the equation; moles of CH_3COOH must be twice moles of Mg.)

Unreacted moles of magnesium = 0.0417 − 0.025 = 0.0167 ✓

Examiner's comments

The mistake is quite a common one, to use $Z = 12$ for magnesium instead of $A_r = 24$. After the mistake, if the chemistry is correct and the calculation is continued using the wrong numerical value, the mistake is penalised only once. So 4 out of 5 marks could be awarded. If an incorrect answer had been given without showing any working, then no marks would have been awarded.

Model answer

Moles of Mg = $\dfrac{0.5}{24}$ = 0.0208 ✓

M_r of CH_3COOH = 60 ✓ Moles of CH_3COOH = $\dfrac{3}{60}$ = 0.05 ✓

The limiting reagent is magnesium, ✓ because 0.0208 moles of Mg can only react with 0.0416 moles of ethanoic acid, not 0.05.

(Look at the equation; moles of CH_3COOH must be twice moles of Mg.)

Unreacted moles of ethanoic acid = 0.05 − 0.0416 = 0.0084 ✓

TOPIC 7 Electricity and chemistry

Key objectives

- To know that an electric current is due to a flow of electrons from negative to positive
- To recall that when metals and graphite conduct there is no accompanying chemical change
- To know that electrolytic conduction occurs only in the liquid phase and is accompanied by chemical reactions
- To know the general principles of electrolysis
- To be able to describe the specified examples of electrolysis with inert electrodes
- To be able to describe and explain the electrolysis of aqueous copper(II) sulphate with carbon electrodes and copper electrodes
- To be able to predict the products of electrolysis
- To be able to write equations for the reactions at the electrodes
- To be able to describe the specified industrial electrolytic processes
- To be able to describe, with reasons, the use of copper and aluminium in cables and the use of plastics and ceramics as insulators

Key definitions

Electrolyte	A substance that conducts an electric current when molten or dissolved in water, with chemical reactions at the electrodes
Non-electrolyte	A substance that does not conduct in the liquid phase
Weak electrolyte	A poor conductor of electricity because it is only partially ionised – there are mainly molecules, few ions
Strong electrolyte	A good conductor of electricity because it is completely ionised
Electrolysis	The process of passing an electric current through a substance and bringing about a chemical reaction
Electrodes	Pieces of metal or carbon through which the current enters and leaves the electrolyte
Cathode	The negative electrode
Anode	The positive electrode

Key ideas Electrolytic conduction

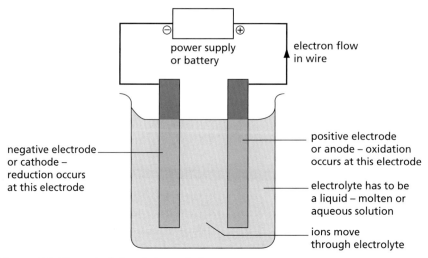

Figure 7.1 The principle of electrolysis

- Electrons flow from the battery to the cathode.
- Positive ions (metallic or hydrogen) in the liquid are attracted to this negative electrode.
- The positive ions accept electrons from the cathode, and metals or hydrogen are formed at the cathode.

$$Cu^{2+} + 2e^- \rightarrow Cu$$
$$2H^+ + 2e^- \rightarrow H_2$$
$$Al^{3+} + 3e^- \rightarrow Al$$

- Electrons flow from the anode to the battery or power supply.
- Negative ions (non-metals except hydrogen) are attracted to this positive electrode.
- When the anode is inert (carbon or platinum) the negative ions lose electrons to the anode.

$$2Cl^- - 2e^- \rightarrow Cl_2 \quad \text{or} \quad 2Cl^- \rightarrow Cl_2 + 2e^-$$
$$4OH^- - 4e^- \rightarrow O_2 + 2H_2O \quad \text{or} \quad 4OH^- \rightarrow O_2 + 2H_2O + 4e^-$$

When the anode is not inert (silver, copper and more reactive metals) the metal atoms of the anode lose electrons and form positive ions. The anode will dissolve and become smaller.

$$Cu - 2e^- \rightarrow Cu^{2+} \quad \text{or} \quad Cu \rightarrow Cu^{2+} + 2e^-$$
$$Zn - 2e^- \rightarrow Zn^{2+} \quad \text{or} \quad Zn \rightarrow Zn^{2+} + 2e^-$$
$$Ag - e^- \rightarrow Ag^+ \quad \text{or} \quad Ag \rightarrow Ag^+ + e^-$$

Water is a very weak electrolyte. Very few water molecules are ionised, so it is a poor conductor of electricity. It is almost entirely molecules with very few ions.

$$H_2O \rightarrow H^+(aq) + OH^-(aq)$$

All aqueous solutions contain hydrogen and hydroxide ions in addition to the ions from the electrolyte. Aqueous sodium chloride contains $Na^+(aq)$, $Cl^-(aq)$, $H^+(aq)$ and $OH^-(aq)$.

Discharge of ions

The ion lower in each of the series will be discharged. The order for positive ions is very similar to the reactivity series of metals (see Topic 18).

Positive ions or cations	Negative ions or anions at an inert electrode
K^+	SO_4^{2-}
Na^+	NO_3^-
Mg^{2+}	OH^-
Al^{3+}	Cl^-
H^+	Br^-
Cu^{2+}	I^-
Ag^+	

Note that Cl^- is discharged in preference to OH^- if the chloride solution is concentrated. If the chloride solution is dilute, then oxygen from OH^- is formed, not chlorine.

35

When the anode is not inert, it will lose electrons and form positive ions in preference to the discharge of a negative ion.

> ### Examiner's tip
> ▶ If you are studying for Paper 2 you are not expected to write ionic equations for the reactions at electrodes. You are expected to predict the products from molten electrolytes and know the products from the electrolysis of concentrated hydrochloric acid and concentrated aqueous sodium chloride.

Examples of electrolysis

● **Molten sodium chloride with inert electrodes**

Ions present: Na^+, Cl^-.

Cathode	Anode
$Na^+ + e^- \rightarrow Na$	$2Cl^- - 2e^- \rightarrow Cl_2$

Sodium chloride is decomposed.

$$2NaCl \rightarrow 2Na + Cl_2$$

● **Aqueous sodium chloride with inert electrodes**

Ions present: $Na^+(aq)$, $Cl^-(aq)$, $H^+(aq)$ and $OH^-(aq)$.

Cathode	Anode
$H^+(aq)$ is lower than $Na^+(aq)$ so $2H^+ + 2e^- \rightarrow H_2$	If solution is concentrated $2Cl^- - 2e^- \rightarrow Cl_2$

Ions left in solution are $Na^+(aq)$ and $OH^-(aq)$. The solution becomes sodium hydroxide.

If the solution is dilute, at the anode:

$$4OH^- - 4e^- \rightarrow O_2 + 2H_2O$$

Ions left in solution are $Na^+(aq)$, $Cl^-(aq)$. Water is used up and the solution becomes more concentrated.

● **Aqueous copper(II) sulphate with carbon electrodes**

Ions present: $Cu^{2+}(aq)$, $SO_4^{2-}(aq)$, $H^+(aq)$ and $OH^-(aq)$.

Cathode	Anode
$Cu^{2+}(aq)$ is lower than $H^+(aq)$ so $Cu^{2+}(aq) + 2e^- \rightarrow Cu$	$OH^-(aq)$ is lower than SO_4^{2-} (aq) so $4OH^- - 4e^- \rightarrow O_2 + 2H_2O$

Ions left in solution are $SO_4^{2-}(aq)$ and $H^+(aq)$. The solution becomes sulphuric acid, H_2SO_4.

● **Aqueous copper(II) sulphate with copper electrodes**

The only difference is at the anode. It is not inert, so it loses electrons and forms ions:

$$Cu - 2e^- \rightarrow Cu^{2+} \quad \text{or} \quad Cu \rightarrow Cu^{2+} + 2e^-$$

Copper is deposited on the cathode which becomes thicker. Copper is removed from anode which gets thinner. The electrolyte remains the same, because one electrode reaction removes copper(II) ions but the other electrode reaction replaces them. This process is used to electroplate other metals with copper and in the refining of copper.

Other examples of electrolysis with inert electrodes

Electrolyte	Cathode reaction	Anode reaction	Change to electrolyte
Molten lead(II) bromide	Lead formed $Pb^{2+} + 2e^- \rightarrow Pb$	Bromine formed $2Br^- - 2e^- \rightarrow Br_2$	Used up
Concentrated hydrochloric acid	Hydrogen formed $2H^+ + 2e^- \rightarrow H_2$	Chlorine formed $2Cl^- - 2e^- \rightarrow Cl_2$	Acid used up
Molten lithium chloride	Lithium formed $Li^+ + e^- \rightarrow Li$	Chlorine formed $2Cl^- - 2e^- \rightarrow Cl_2$	Used up
Dilute sulphuric acid	Hydrogen formed $2H^+ + 2e^- \rightarrow H_2$	Oxygen formed $4OH^- - 4e^- \rightarrow O_2 + 2H_2O$	Water used up, acid becomes more concentrated
Aqueous lead nitrate	Lead formed $Pb^{2+} + 2e^- \rightarrow Pb$	Oxygen formed $4OH^- - 4e^- \rightarrow O_2 + 2H_2O$	H^+(aq) and NO_3^-(aq) left. Solution changes to nitric acid
Aqueous potassium bromide	Hydrogen formed $2H^+ + 2e^- \rightarrow H_2$	Bromine formed $2Br^- - 2e^- \rightarrow Br_2$	Solution changes to potassium hydroxide

Extraction of aluminium

Examiner's tips
▶ You do not have to learn to draw this diagram but you may be asked to label it.
▶ For Paper 2 you will need to know that aluminium is formed at the cathode and oxygen at the anode.
▶ You will also need to know the uses of electroplating (see p. 38) and be able to describe the process without writing equations.

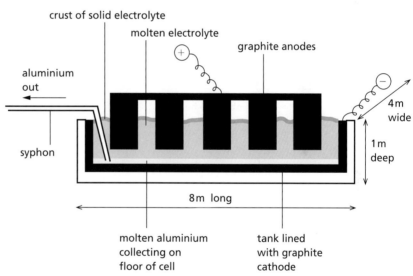

Figure 7.2 The industrial extraction of aluminium by electrolysis

Essential information is:

- the main ore of aluminium is bauxite
- it is changed into pure aluminium oxide, alumina
- both cathode and anodes are carbon (graphite)
- the electrolyte is a molten mixture, pure aluminium oxide dissolved in cryolite, Na_3AlF_6
- the temperature of the molten electrolyte is about 900 °C
- at the cathode $Al^{3+} + 3e^- \rightarrow Al$
- at the anode $2O^{2-} - 4e^- \rightarrow O_2$
- the carbon anodes burn away in the oxygen and have to be replaced periodically
- the cryolite lowers the temperature from over 2000 °C, the melting point of aluminium oxide, to about 900 °C. This leads to a large saving in energy. It also improves the electrical conductivity of the electrolyte.

Industrial electrolysis of aqueous sodium chloride

The electrolysis has already been described. You do not have to know details of the cell. The products are chlorine, hydrogen and sodium hydroxide. These have the following uses.

Chlorine	Hydrogen	Sodium hydroxide
In making solvents	In the Haber process	To make soaps
For treating drinking water	To make margarine	In extraction of aluminium
As a bleach	As a fuel in fuel cells	To make soapless detergents
In making plastics, PVC	As rocket fuel	In textiles manufacture

Electroplating

This is used to plate one metal with another. The general arrangement for electroplating is shown in Figure 7.3.

The electrolysis has been described earlier. The metals commonly used to electroplate are copper, chromium, nickel, tin and silver. The two main reasons for electroplating are appearance (highly polished shiny finish) and protection from corrosion and abrasion. Chromium plating, for example, gives a pleasing appearance, and because chromium is very hard it is resistant to scratching and it protects the underlying metal from corrosion.

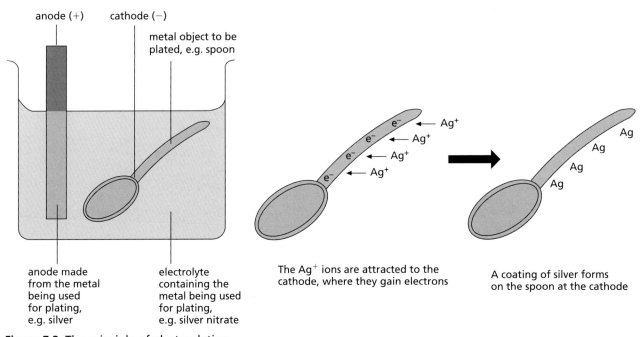

anode (+) cathode (−)

metal object to be plated, e.g. spoon

anode made from the metal being used for plating, e.g. silver

electrolyte containing the metal being used for plating, e.g. silver nitrate

The Ag$^+$ ions are attracted to the cathode, where they gain electrons

A coating of silver forms on the spoon at the cathode

Figure 7.3 The principle of electroplating

Refining

Metals can be refined or purified by electrolysis. The impure metal forms the anode, the cathode is a small piece of the pure metal and the electrolyte is an aqueous metal salt. In the refining of copper, Figure 7.4, the following reactions occur.

Cathode	Anode
Copper ions from the solution lose their charge and copper is deposited $Cu^{2+}(aq) + 2e^- \rightarrow Cu$	Copper atoms lose their valency electrons and go into solution as ions $Cu - 2e^- \rightarrow Cu^{2+}$ or $Cu \rightarrow Cu^{2+} + 2e^-$

The overall effect is that pure copper is transferred from the anode to the cathode. The impurities from the copper are left as 'anode slime' and the cathode becomes a large piece of pure copper.

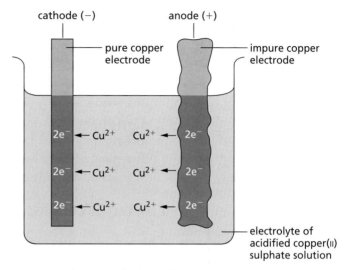

Figure 7.4 The purification of copper by electrolysis

Sample questions and answers

Sample question 1 Describe what you would see when aqueous copper(II) sulphate is electrolysed using carbon electrodes.   [4 marks]

Model answer A colourless gas, ✓ oxygen, is formed at the anode.

A brown deposit of copper ✓ at the cathode.

The solution changes from blue ✓ to colourless. ✓

> **Examiner's tips**
> ▶ Take care to answer the question. Here you must state what would be *seen*.
> ▶ You are advised to specify what occurs at each electrode.
> ▶ *Colourless* is essential here, *clear* is wrong – you can have a clear blue solution.

Sample question 2 Magnesium is manufactured by the electrolysis of its **molten** chloride. Explain why it cannot be obtained by the electrolysis of its **aqueous** chloride, by giving the reactions at the electrodes in both cases.   [6 marks]

Model answer In an aqueous solution of magnesium chloride, Mg^{2+} and H^+ ✓ move to the cathode. Hydrogen is formed. ✓

At the cathode $2H^+ + 2e^- \rightarrow H_2$ ✓   *(The hydrogen ions are from the water.)*

The only positive ions in molten magnesium chloride are Mg^{2+}. ✓

At the cathode $\quad Mg^{2+} + 2e^- \rightarrow Mg$ ✓

At the anode (in both cases) $2Cl^- - 2e^- \rightarrow Cl_2$ ✓

● **Try this** *The answers are given on p. 121.*

1 Name the three products formed when aqueous potassium iodide, KI, is electrolysed using inert electrodes. Give equations for the reactions at the electrodes and explain why the solution becomes alkaline. [6 marks]

2 Describe how you would copper plate a nickel spoon by completing the following.

The anode is ......
The cathode is ......
The electrolyte is ......
The equation for the anode reaction is ......
The equation for the cathode reaction is ...... [5 marks]

Electrical cables: conductors and insulators

● **Conductors** The reasons for using copper are:

- it is a very good conductor of electricity
- it is ductile, that is, easily drawn into thin wires
- the metal is easily purified (impurities greatly decrease the electrical conductivity).

The reasons for using aluminium are:

- it is a good conductor of electricity
- it resists corrosion
- it has a low density so higher diameter cables can be used, thus reducing the resistance while reducing the risk of sagging.

Aluminium cables have a steel core which further reduces the risk of sagging and breaking.

● **Insulators** The most common insulators are plastics, for example poly(chloroethene) or PVC. Reasons for using plastics are:

- they do not conduct electricity
- they are flexible and easily moulded
- they are non-biodegradable.

Ceramics (clay materials, like pottery) are also used to make certain insulators. Ceramics are suitable as insulators because:

- they do not conduct electricity
- they have high melting points so they can be used at high temperatures
- they are not affected by water or oxygen
- they can be moulded into complex shapes.

TOPIC 8 Chemical changes and energy

Key objectives

- To know that there are different forms of energy – heat, chemical, electrical, nuclear and light
- To know the meanings of exothermic and endothermic
- To be able to describe the production of heat energy by burning fuels
- To assess hydrogen as a fuel
- To know that radioactive isotopes, such as ^{235}U, are a source of energy
- To know that bond breaking is endothermic and bond forming is exothermic
- Given the appropriate data, to be able to perform simple calculations on the energetics of bond breaking and forming
- To be able to describe the production of electrical energy from simple cells
- To be able to describe batteries as a convenient and portable power source

Key ideas

Exothermic and endothermic reactions

An *exothermic* reaction gives out heat. The chemical energy of the reactants is bigger than the chemical energy of the products. This difference in chemical energy is transferred to the surroundings as heat energy.

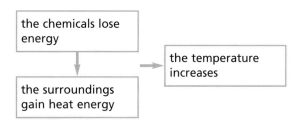

An *endothermic* reaction takes in heat. The chemical energy of the reactants is smaller than that of the products so this difference in energy is transferred from the surroundings to the chemicals.

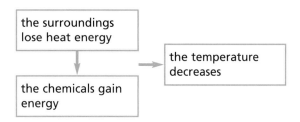

Production of heat energy

The most common way of producing heat energy is by burning fossil fuels – natural gas, coal and petroleum products. See Topic 23.

41

Heat energy and then electrical energy is produced from nuclear reactors. An example of a nuclear fuel is the radioactive isotope ^{235}U.

Hydrogen as a fuel

The combustion of hydrogen is highly exothermic. It is only used as a rocket fuel, in experimental vehicles and in fuel cells. The advantages and disadvantages of hydrogen as a fuel are given in the following table.

Advantages	Disadvantages
It is the most energy-rich fuel – it releases more energy per kilogram than any other conventional (non-nuclear) fuel	It is expensive to produce
The only product of the combustion is water $2H_2 + O_2 \rightarrow 2H_2O$ No pollutants are formed	It is difficult to store – storage under high pressure, as a liquid, or absorption under pressure in suitable metallic compounds are all expensive options
Oxides of nitrogen are not produced by the combustion. These oxides are particularly harmful pollutants which form nitric acid in the atmosphere, a constituent of acid rain	

Bond breaking and forming

Bond breaking requires energy – it is endothermic.

> **Examiner's tip**
> ▶ Energy is measured in kilojoules (kJ). You are not required to know these units but they will probably be used in any calculation.

The bond energy of a C–H bond is 413 kJ/mol. To break one mole of C–H bonds +413 kJ is supplied to the chemicals (+ because there is an increase in chemical energy).

Bond forming is exothermic. To form one mole of C–H bonds −413 kJ are lost by the chemicals.

Sample question 1 Show that the following reaction is exothermic.

$$CH_4 + F_2 \rightarrow CH_3F + H–F$$

Bond energies: C–H 413, F–F 158, H–F 565, and C–F 495, all in kJ/mol. [3 marks]

Model answer

Bonds broken	Bonds formed
1 C–H = +413	1 C–F = −495
1 F–F = +158	1 H–F = −565
Total = +571 kJ ✓	Total = −1060 kJ ✓
Endothermic	Exothermic

The exothermic energy change is bigger than the endothermic change, so the reaction is exothermic. ✓

Electrolysis

In electrolysis electrical energy is supplied; the reactions are endothermic. Electrical energy is changed into chemical energy.

Cells

A cell produces electrical energy; the reactions are exothermic. Chemical energy is changed into electrical energy.

A cell consists of two different metals in a solution of an electrolyte, Figure 8.1.

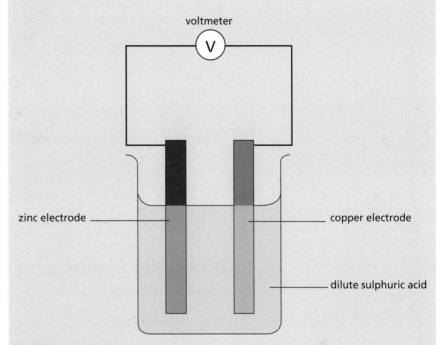

Figure 8.1 A simple cell

The more reactive metal, here zinc, goes into solution as ions.

$$Zn(s) \rightarrow Zn^{2+}(aq) + 2e^-$$

The electrons flow through the wire and the voltmeter to the copper electrode. At this electrode, hydrogen ions from the electrolyte form hydrogen gas.

$$2H^+(aq) + 2e^- \rightarrow H_2(g)$$

The exothermic reaction can be represented by an ionic equation:

$$Zn(s) + 2H^+(aq) \rightarrow Zn^{2+}(aq) + H_2(g)$$

metal   from acid   zinc salt   bubbles of gas

Cells will be discussed again in Topic 18.

Fuel cells

In the simple cell above, the zinc electrode reacts with the electrolyte to produce electrical energy. When one of these reactants is used up, the cell does not supply any more energy. In a fuel cell there are two electrodes, usually containing platinum, in an electrolyte, and the reactants are continuously supplied to the electrodes (Figure 8.2). This type of cell can supply electrical energy continuously.

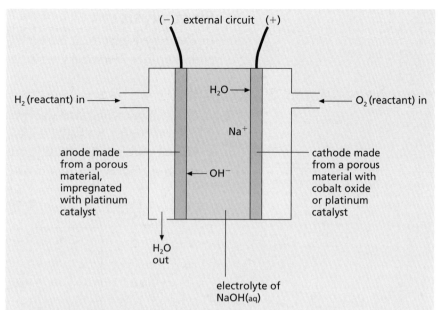

Figure 8.2 Diagrammatic view of a fuel cell

At the negative electrode hydrogen is supplied, the molecules lose electrons and form ions in the electrolyte.

$$H_2(g) \rightarrow 2H^+(aq) + 2e^-$$

The electrons move through the external circuit to the positive electrode, to which oxygen is supplied.

$$O_2 + 2H_2O + 4e^- \rightarrow 4OH^-(aq)$$

The ions formed react to produce water.

$$H^+(aq) + OH^-(aq) \rightarrow H_2O$$

The overall reaction is:

$$2H_2 + O_2 \rightarrow 2H_2O$$

When hydrogen is burnt in oxygen to form water, heat energy is produced. When hydrogen reacts with oxygen to form water in a fuel cell, electrical energy is produced.

Cells (batteries) and fuel cells prove a portable and convenient source of power. Hydrogen fuel cells are used in space to provide the electrical power for space shuttles and other space vehicles. Batteries have many uses, for example in torches, calculators and portable CD players.

Questions on cells are included in Topic 18.

TOPIC 9 Chemical reactions: speed of reaction

Key objectives

- To know the factors that affect reaction rate
- To be able to explain the effect of temperature and concentration on reaction rate in terms of the collision theory
- To be able to describe a practical method to investigate the speed of a reaction that involves the evolution of a gas
- To devise suitable methods of investigating the effect of a given variable on reaction rate
- To interpret data on reaction rates
- To be able to describe the danger of explosive combustion with fine powders (flour mills) and gases (coal mining)
- To be able to describe the effect of light on the reduction of silver(I) salts in photography and on the rate of photosynthesis

Key ideas

Reaction rate

The best definition of reaction rate is:

$$\text{rate} = \frac{\text{change in concentration of a reactant}}{\text{time}}$$

This emphasises that the rate depends on concentration and not on the amount of reactant.

Factors that affect reaction rate

> **Examiner's tip**
> ► If you are studying for Paper 2 you do not have to know the collision theory for reaction rates. You are only required to know that when the concentration is increased, the rate is increased and vice versa.

● **Collision theory** A reaction will occur when particles collide and they have enough energy to react. Reaction rate depends on the collision rate of the reactant particles and the energy of these particles.

● **Concentration** When the concentration is increased, the rate is increased and vice versa.

Increasing the concentration of a reactant increases the number of reacting particles in unit volume (the number of particles/dm^3), so the collision rate will increase as well as the rate of reaction.

> **Examiner's tip**
> ► Remember to write that the concentration has decreased NOT just that the reactant has been used up. Rate depends on the concentration of the reactants not on the amount.

● **Temperature** When the temperature is increased, the rate will increase, and the rate will decrease when the temperature is decreased.

> When the temperature is increased the particles have more energy so more of the colliding particles will have the necessary energy to react. Also, because the particles are moving faster, they will collide more frequently – the collision rate has increased. Both of these two explanations are valid.

● **Pressure** The pressure only affects reactions involving gases. The rate will increase when the pressure is increased.

> When the pressure is increased, the gaseous molecules are closer together so they collide more frequently and the reaction rate increases.

● **Catalyst** A catalyst increases the rate of a reaction but remains chemically unchanged. Enzymes are biological catalysts. (Refer to fermentation in Topic 25, p. 112.)

● **Particle size** This only affects reactions involving solids. A fine powder has a larger surface area than a single lump of the same mass (Figure 9.1). The larger surface area increases the collision rate and hence the rate of reaction.

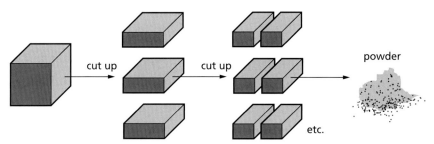

Figure 9.1 A powder has a larger surface area

In any industry where there are fine combustible powders, such as flour, fine metallic dust from metal working and coal dust in mines, there is real risk of an explosion due to the very rapid combustion of the powder. In coal mines, there is the additional hazard of methane gas, which when mixed with air will explode.

Reactions with light

There are two important examples of photochemical reactions.

● **Reduction of a silver(I) halide** This is the basis of photography. A photographic film is coated with a layer of silver(I) bromide. When this is exposed to light, silver ions accept electrons from bromide ions and form silver atoms. This is reduction (which will be explained in Topic 11).

$$Ag^+ + e^- \rightarrow Ag$$
white   black

Parts of the film that have been exposed to light go black, while unexposed parts stay white. The rate of this reaction depends on the intensity or brightness of the light.

● Photosynthesis   Green plants make carbohydrates by this reaction.

carbon dioxide + water → glucose + oxygen
from air   through   changes into
                 roots   more complex
                 from soil   carbohydrate

$$6CO_2 + 6H_2O \rightarrow C_6H_{12}O_6 + 6O_2$$

The reaction is catalysed by the green pigment in the plants, chlorophyll, and only occurs in sunlight. It is photochemical and its rate depends on the intensity of the incident light.

Experimental methods

When a gas is one of the products, it can be collected in a gas syringe and its volume measured every minute. For example, sodium chlorate(I) decomposes to form sodium chloride and oxygen. The rate of this reaction can be measured by measuring the volume of oxygen at regular intervals of time, Figure 9.2.

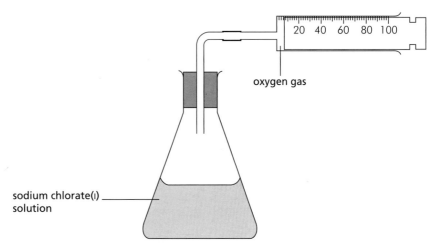

Figure 9.2 Collecting the gas

The volume of gas is plotted against time. The slope or gradient of this graph, at a certain time, measures the reaction rate at that time. See Figure 9.3.

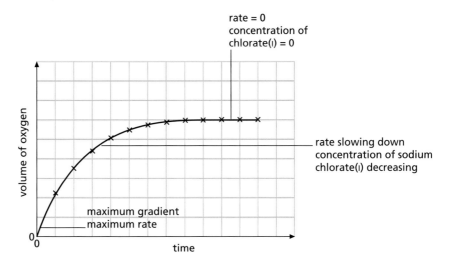

Figure 9.3 Determining reaction rate from a graph of volume of gas

An alternative method to collecting a gaseous product, is to allow the gas to escape and to measure the mass of apparatus and chemicals every minute, Figure 9.4. The total mass will decrease as the gas escapes. The loss of mass equals the mass of gas produced. The total mass, or the loss of mass, can be plotted against time. See Figure 9.5a, b. The slope or gradient of these graphs, at a certain time, measures the rate of reaction at that time.

When a solid reacts with a solution, the time taken for the solid to react completely can be measured. A suitable reaction for this method is:

$$CaCO_3(s) + 2HCl(aq) \rightarrow CaCl_2(aq) + CO_2(g) + H_2O(l)$$

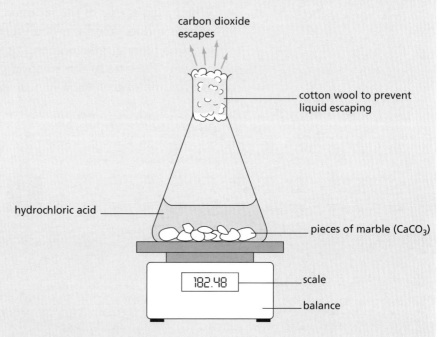

Figure 9.4 Measuring the mass

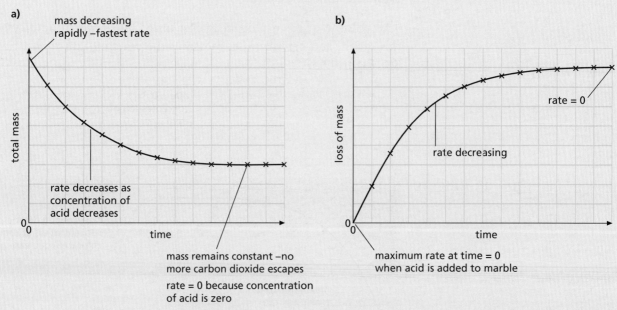

Figure 9.5 Determining reaction rate from graphs of **a)** mass or **b)** loss of mass

Sample question and answers

Sample question 1 $20\,cm^3$ of hydrochloric acid, concentration $1.0\,mol/dm^3$, was added to $20\,g$ of calcium carbonate (large pieces) in a conical flask. The mass of the flask and chemicals was measured every minute. The mass decreased as the carbon dioxide escaped.

$$CaCO_3(s) + 2HCl(aq) \rightarrow CaCl_2(aq) + CO_2(g) + H_2O(l)$$

The loss of mass was plotted against time.

a) Calculate the number of moles of calcium carbonate and of hydrochloric acid to show that the hydrochloric acid was the limiting reagent. [3 marks]

b) The reaction rate, mass of carbon dioxide/time, is the slope of the curve. Why does this rate decrease with time? [2 marks]

c) How and why would the graph differ if the experiment was repeated using $20.0\,g$ of smaller pieces of calcium carbonate? [2 marks]

d) How would the graph differ if the experiment was repeated using $20\,cm^3$ of hydrochloric acid, of concentration $2.0\,mol/dm^3$? [2 marks]

Model answers **a)** Moles of HCl = $\frac{20}{1000} \times 1 = 0.02$ ✓

Moles of $CaCO_3$ = $\frac{20}{100} = 0.2$ ✓

All the acid is used, ✓ so this is the limiting reagent.

b) Because the concentration ✓ of the acid is decreasing. ✓

Examiner's comment *'Acid used up' would only have been given 1 mark. Rates depend on concentration not on amount.*

Model answers **c)** Bigger surface area so rate faster ✓ and the graph steeper at the beginning. ✓

> **Examiner's tip**
> ▶ If you are asked about a graph as here, the marks are awarded for comments about the shape of the graph. Remember marks are not awarded for correct chemistry but for correct chemistry that answers the question.

d) Double the concentration of the acid, the initial rate is twice as fast, the graph has twice the slope ✓ at the origin. Double the number of moles of the limiting reagent, double the mass of carbon dioxide. The graph finishes at double the height on y axis. ✓

● **Try this** *The answers are given on p. 121.*

1 A piece of magnesium was added to 100 cm³ of hydrochloric acid. The time taken for the metal to react completely was measured. The experiment was repeated using the same volume of acid and identical pieces of magnesium. The results are given in the table.

Experiment	Concentration of acid in mol/dm³	Time in seconds
1	1.0	60
2	1.0	30
3	2.0	....
4	....	240

a) Suggest a reason why the rate of experiment 2 is faster than that of experiment 1.   [1 mark]

b) Using the results of experiment 1 as standard for comparison, complete the table.   [2 marks]

2 Describe how you could show that manganese(IV) oxide, which is an insoluble powder, can catalyse the decomposition of aqueous hydrogen peroxide. Give brief details of the apparatus you would use, the measurements you would make, how you would ensure that your experiments were a 'fair test' and how the data would show that the manganese(IV) oxide was a catalyst.

$$2H_2O_2(aq) \rightarrow 2H_2O(l) + O_2(g)$$ [8 marks]

3 A piece of paper was coated with silver(I) bromide. It was used in the experiment shown in Figure 9.6.

a) Explain why the two areas are different colours at the end of the experiment.   [2 marks]

b) How would the appearance of the paper change if it were now exposed to the light again? Give a reason for your answer. [2 marks]

c) Write an ionic equation for the reaction.   [1 mark]

d) What difference, and why, would using a dimmer light in this experiment make?   [2 marks]

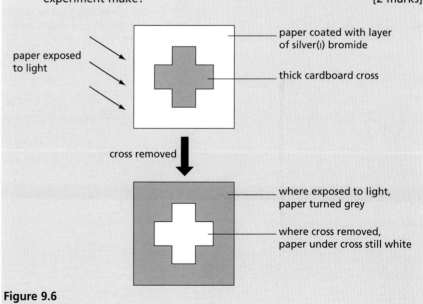

paper exposed to light

paper coated with layer of silver(I) bromide

thick cardboard cross

cross removed

where exposed to light, paper turned grey

where cross removed, paper under cross still white

Figure 9.6

TOPIC 10 Reversible reactions

Key objectives

- To know that some reactions are reversible
- To know that the thermal decomposition of some hydrated salts is reversible
- To understand the concept of equilibrium
- To be able to predict the effect of changing conditions on the position of equilibrium

Key ideas

Reversible reactions

When hydrated copper(II) sulphate is heated, it decomposes.

$$CuSO_4.5H_2O(s) \rightarrow CuSO_4(s) + 5H_2O(g)$$

blue crystals   white powder

This is the forward reaction, which is endothermic; heat energy is supplied.

When the products are cooled and mixed, the reverse reaction occurs.

$$CuSO_4(s) + 5H_2O(l) \rightarrow CuSO_4.5H_2O(s)$$

white powder   blue crystals

This is the reverse reaction, which is exothermic; heat energy is given off.

The reversible reaction can be written as one equation:

$$\overset{\text{heat}}{CuSO_4.5H_2O(s) \underset{\text{cool and mix}}{\rightleftharpoons} CuSO_4(s) + 5H_2O(l)}$$

Equilibrium

Important ideas are:

- reversible reactions can come to equilibrium
- at equilibrium, the rate of the forward and of the reverse reaction are equal
- at equilibrium, the concentrations of reactants and products do not change (unless the conditions are changed).

These equilibrium concentrations are referred to as the *position of equilibrium*. If the position of equilibrium moves to the right, in the new equilibrium mixture the concentration of products has increased and that of the reactants has decreased.

Reaction conditions and the position of equilibrium

Concentration   When the concentration of a product is decreased, the position of equilibrium will move to the right (as if to replace the missing reagent).

When the concentration of a product is increased, the position of equilibrium will move to the left (as if to remove the extra product).

A similar situation applies to changes in the concentration of a reactant.

$$BiCl_3(aq) + H_2O(l) \rightleftharpoons BiOCl(s) + 2HCl(aq)$$
colourless   white

If the concentration of hydrochloric acid in the equilibrium mixture is increased, the position of equilibrium moves to the left and the amount of white solid in the new equilibrium mixture is reduced.

● **Temperature** In a reversible reaction one reaction is exothermic and the other is equally endothermic.

Decreasing the temperature (removal of heat energy) will favour the exothermic change (gives out heat energy).

Increasing the temperature (addition of heat energy) will favour the endothermic change (takes in heat energy). Note the reaction tries to remove the change in conditions.

For the reaction

$$N_2(g) + O_2(g) \rightleftharpoons 2NO(g)$$

the forward reaction is endothermic. Increasing the temperature will move the position of equilibrium to the right. The new equilibrium mixture will have a higher concentration of nitrogen oxide.

● **Pressure** This is only a factor for reactions that involve gases.

Increasing the pressure will move the position of equilibrium to the side with the smaller volume (of gases) or with the smaller number of gaseous molecules.

Decreasing the pressure will move the position of equilibrium to the side with the larger volume (of gases) or with the larger number of gaseous molecules.

$$N_2(g) + 3H_2(g) \rightleftharpoons 2NH_3(g)$$
4 molecules of gas   2 molecules of gas
or 4 volumes   or 2 volumes

A decrease in pressure in the above reaction will move the position of equilibrium to the left. There will be less ammonia in the new equilibrium mixture. An increase in pressure will move the position of equilibrium to the right, and there will be more ammonia in the equilibrium mixture.

● **Catalysts** These have no effect on the position of equilibrium, only on the rate of reaction.

There will be further discussion of equilibria and questions in Topics 20 and 21.

Examiner's tip
▶ Remember the reaction always tries to oppose the change in conditions.

● **Try this** *The answers are given on p. 122.*

1 What would be the effect on the position of equilibrium (move to right, move to left or no change) of increasing the pressure on the following equilibria? Give a reason for your choice.

equilibrium 1 $H_2(g) + I_2(g) \rightleftharpoons 2HI(g)$
equilibrium 2 $2SO_2(g) + O_2(g) \rightleftharpoons 2SO_3(g)$
equilibrium 3 $N_2O_4(g) \rightleftharpoons 2NO_2(g)$ [6 marks]

2 Explain why the following reversible reaction cannot come to equilibrium when calcium carbonate is heated in an open test tube.

$$CaCO_3(s) \rightleftharpoons CaO(s) + CO_2(g)$$ [2 marks]

3 Describe the effect on the position of equilibrium of this reaction by each of the following changes.

$$CO(g) + 2H_2(g) \rightleftharpoons CH_3OH(g) \quad \text{forward reaction is exothermic}$$

i) adding a catalyst
ii) increasing the pressure
iii) adding more hydrogen
iv) increasing the temperature   [4 marks]

4 Iodine monochloride reacts with chlorine in a reversible reaction to form iodine trichloride.

$$ICl(l) \ + \ Cl_2(g) \ \rightleftharpoons \ ICl_3(s)$$
  brown   yellow

The equilibrium mixture contains both the brown liquid and the yellow solid.
i) What would you see if more chlorine was added to the mixture?   [2 marks]
ii) What would you see if the chlorine was allowed to leave the equilibrium mixture?   [2 marks]
iii) What would be the effect, if any, of increasing the pressure? Give a reason for your answer.   [2 marks]
iv) When the mixture is heated the yellow solid disappears. What can you deduce about the forward reaction?   [2 marks]

5 When bromine is dissolved in water the following equilibrium is set up.

$$Br_2 \ + \ H_2O \ \rightleftharpoons \ Br^- \ + \ BrO^- \ + \ 2H^+$$
  brown   all these ions are colourless

For each of the following additions, predict whether the brown colour would become darker, stay the same or go lighter. Give a reason for each.
i) Add some crystals of potassium bromide.   [2 marks]
ii) Add a few drops of hydrochloric acid.   [2 marks]
iii) Add a few drops of aqueous sodium hydroxide.   [3 marks]

TOPIC 11 Redox

Key objectives
- To be able to define oxidation and reduction in terms of gain and loss of oxygen
- To be familiar with the terms reducing agent and oxidising agent
- To use the idea of oxidation state to name ions
- To be able to define redox in terms of electron transfer
- To identify redox reactions by changes in oxidation state
- To be able to recall the colour changes involved with acidified potassium manganate(VII) and potassium iodide

Key ideas ## Oxidation and reduction

Oxidation is the gain of oxygen. Reduction is the loss of oxygen. For example:

$$\underset{\text{oxidation}}{\underset{\overbrace{\qquad\qquad\qquad}}{\overset{\text{reduction}}{\overbrace{\qquad\qquad\qquad}}}}$$

$$CuO \ + \ H_2 \rightarrow Cu + H_2O$$

Copper(II) oxide is reduced to copper by hydrogen. Hydrogen is the *reducing agent* in this redox reaction.

Hydrogen has been oxidised to water by the copper(II) oxide. Copper(II) oxide is the *oxidising agent* or oxidant.

Electron transfer

Oxidation is the loss of electrons. Reduction is the gain of electrons.

> **Examiner's tips**
> ▶ Remember OILRIG:
>
>   Oxidation Is the Loss of electrons.
>   Reduction Is the Gain of electrons.
>
> ▶ Knowing this mnemonic almost guarantees that you will gain some marks in this type of question.

Sample question 1
a) Write a symbol equation for the displacement of copper from copper(II) sulphate by the more reactive metal, zinc. [1 mark]
b) Write an ionic equation for the same reaction. [2 marks]
c) In terms of electron transfer, identify the change which is oxidation. [2 marks]
d) Which reactant is the oxidising agent or oxidant? Give a reason for your choice. [2 marks]

Examiner's comments *For parts (c) and (d), 1 mark is given for the correct choice and 1 for the reason in terms of electron transfer. In the following model answer, too much information has been given but as it is all correct the examiner will pick out the marking points.*

Model answer

a) $Zn + CuSO_4 \rightarrow ZnSO_4 + Cu$ ✓

b) $Zn + Cu^{2+} + SO_4^{2-} \rightarrow Zn^{2+} + SO_4^{2-} + Cu$

The sulphate ion is common to both sides; it has taken no part in the reaction. The ionic equation is

$Zn + Cu^{2+}$ ✓ $\rightarrow Zn^{2+} + Cu$ ✓

c) The zinc atom has lost two electrons; ✓ it has been oxidised.

$Zn \rightarrow Zn^{2+} + 2e^-$ This is oxidation. ✓

d) $Cu^{2+} + 2e^- \rightarrow Cu$

The copper(II) ion has gained the two electrons which were lost by the zinc. ✓ Zinc atoms were oxidised by copper(II) ions. Copper(II) ions are the oxidising agent or oxidant. ✓

Oxidation states

You are only required to use these to name ions and to recognise oxidation and reduction.

Typical examples are Fe^{2+} iron(II) or Fe(+2), Fe^{3+} iron(III) or Fe(+3), Cu^{2+} copper(II) or Cu(+2), manganate(VII) or Mn(+7) and dichromate(VI) or Cr(+6).

The above oxidation states are all positive and can be thought of as a real or imaginary charge. Any uncombined element has an oxidation state of 0. Oxidation states can be negative, for example I(−1) and S(−2).

An increase in oxidation state is oxidation; a decrease is reduction.

Colour changes and oxidation states

● Potassium iodide to iodine – colourless to brown.
● Potassium manganate(VII) to a manganese(II) salt – purple to colourless.

Sample question 2

Write a balanced equation for the reaction between iron(III) oxide and carbon monoxide. Identify the change which is reduction and the oxidant. [4 marks]

Model answer

$Fe_2O_3 + 3CO \rightarrow 2Fe + 3CO_2$ ✓✓ *(1 mark for correct formulae and 1 mark for correct balancing.)*

Fe_2O_3 to 2Fe is reduction. ✓ The iron(III) oxide has lost oxygen.

Fe_2O_3 is the oxidant. ✓ It oxidised carbon monoxide to carbon dioxide.

● **Try this**   *The answers are given on p. 122.*

1 a) Complete the equation for the reaction between aluminium and iron(III) oxide.

$$Al + Fe_2O_3 \rightarrow$$ [2 marks]

   b) Which reactant is the oxidant? Explain your choice.   [2 marks]
   c) Which change is reduction? Give a reason.   [2 marks]

2 Write an equation for the redox reaction between lead(IV) oxide and hydrogen. Identify the change that is oxidation and the reactant that is the oxidant.   [4 marks]

3 For the following redox reaction write half equations, showing the electron transfer. Then identify the change which is oxidation and the reactant which is the reducing agent. Give a reason for each answer.

$$Cl_2 + 2I^- \rightarrow 2Cl^- + I_2$$ [6 marks]

4 Decide whether the following changes are oxidation, reduction or neither.
   i)   potassium dichromate(VI) to chromium(III) chloride
   ii) tin to tin(IV) chloride
   iii) chlorine to chloride(–1)
   iv) copper(II) oxide to copper(II) chloride   [4 marks]

5 Magnesium can displace silver from its salts.

$$Mg + 2AgNO_3 \rightarrow Mg(NO_3)_2 + 2Ag$$

   a) What is the valency of silver and what is the formula of the silver ion?   [2 marks]

Examiner's tip
▶ You cannot predict this valency from the periodic table. You must work it out from the formula of silver nitrate.

   b) What is the valency of magnesium and what is the formula of the magnesium ion?   [2 marks]
   c) Write an ionic equation for this reaction.   [2 marks]
   d) Write an ionic equation for the change that is reduction. [1 mark]
   e) Which reactant is the reducing agent? Give a reason.   [2 marks]

TOPIC 12 Properties of acids and bases

Key objectives
- To be able to describe the typical properties of acids
- To be able to describe the typical properties of bases
- To be able to define acids and bases in terms of proton transfer
- To know the difference between weak and strong acids and between weak and strong bases
- To understand the pH scale
- To know the importance of controlling the pH of soil
- To be able to classify metallic oxides as basic and non-metallic oxides as acidic
- To be able to extend this classification to neutral and amphoteric oxides

Key ideas

Properties of acids

A simple definition of an acid is that it forms hydrogen ions, $H^+(aq)$, when dissolved in water.

Most metals react with an acid to form a salt and hydrogen. See Topic 18.

$$Mg + 2HCl \rightarrow MgCl_2 + H_2$$

$$Mg(s) + 2H^+(aq) \rightarrow Mg^{2+}(aq) + H_2(g)$$

Acids are neutralised by bases, which are metal oxides and hydroxides, to form salts and water.

copper(II) oxide + sulphuric acid $\rightarrow$ copper(II) sulphate + water

$$CuO + H_2SO_4 \rightarrow CuSO_4 + H_2O$$

$$CuO(s) + 2H^+(aq) \rightarrow Cu^{2+}(aq) + H_2O(l)$$

The base ammonia neutralises acids to form ammonium salts.

ammonia + nitric acid $\rightarrow$ ammonium nitrate

$$NH_3(aq) + HNO_3 \rightarrow NH_4NO_3(aq)$$

Salts are formed when the acidic hydrogen atoms of an acid are replaced by a metal or by an ammonium group. The replacement can be direct, as when magnesium chloride is formed from magnesium metal and hydrochloric acid, or indirect, as when the acid is neutralised by a base, for example the reaction between magnesium oxide and hydrochloric acid.

Carbonates react with acids to form a salt, carbon dioxide and water.

calcium carbonate + hydrochloric acid $\rightarrow$ calcium chloride + carbon dioxide + water

$$Na_2CO_3 + 2HNO_3 \rightarrow 2NaNO_3 + CO_2 + H_2O$$

$$CuCO_3(s) + 2H^+(aq) \rightarrow Cu^{2+}(aq) + CO_2(g) + H_2O(l)$$

Acids turn blue litmus paper red.

Typical properties of bases

A simple definition of a base is that it can neutralise an acid by accepting hydrogen ions. Bases that are soluble in water are called alkalis. An aqueous alkali contains the hydroxide ion, $OH^-(aq)$.

A base can neutralise an acid to form a salt (and water).

$$NaOH(aq) + HCl(aq) \rightarrow NaCl(aq) + H_2O(l)$$

The ionic equation for this reaction is obtained as follows. The first three chemicals are strong electrolytes so they are written as ions. Water is a very weak electrolyte that exists mainly as molecules.

$$Na^+(aq) + OH^-(aq) + H^+(aq) + Cl^-(aq) \rightarrow$$
$$Na^+(aq) + Cl^-(aq) + H_2O(l)$$

The ions that have not reacted are cancelled, giving

$$OH^-(aq) + H^+(aq) \rightarrow H_2O(l)$$

This is the ionic equation for any alkali being neutralised by any strong acid.

Alkalis react with ammonium salts to form a salt, ammonia and water.

$$\text{ammonium chloride} + \text{sodium hydroxide} \rightarrow \text{sodium chloride} + \text{ammonia} + \text{water}$$

$$NH_4Cl + NaOH \rightarrow NaCl + NH_3 + H_2O$$

$$NH_4^+ + OH^- \rightarrow NH_3 + H_2O$$

This the ionic equation for any ammonium salt reacting with any alkali.

Alkalis or soluble bases turn red litmus paper blue. Insoluble bases have no effect on litmus paper.

Definitions of acids and bases

Acids and bases have already been defined in terms of the transfer of hydrogen ions, $H^+(aq)$. A more modern definition defines them in terms of the transfer of protons, H^+. An acid is a proton donor and a base is a proton acceptor.

$$\underset{\text{acid}}{NH_4^+} + \underset{\text{base}}{OH^-} \rightarrow NH_3 + H_2O$$

The ammonium ion loses a proton (H^+) and becomes ammonia. The hydroxide ion accepts a proton and becomes water.

The pH scale

The pH scale shows whether a substance is acidic, alkaline or neutral. It will also show how acidic or alkaline the substance is.

- pH = 7: neutral, for example pure water
- pH < 7: acidic
- the lower the pH, the more acidic is the solution and the greater its concentration of $H^+(aq)$
- pH > 7: alkaline

- the higher the pH, the more alkaline is the solution and the greater its concentration of OH⁻(aq).

The pH of a substance can be measured using universal indicator. The colour of the indicator is matched against the pH scale. Alternatively, a pH meter can be used.

pH	0 1	2 3	4 5 6	7	8 9 10	11 12	13 14
	strong acid	weak acid	very weak acid	neutral	very weak base	weak base	strong base

Figure 12.1 The range of the pH scale

Strong and weak acids

Examples of strong acids are hydrochloric acid, sulphuric acid and nitric acid. In aqueous solution these are completely ionised – all ions, no molecules.

$$HCl(aq) \rightarrow H^+(aq) + Cl^-(aq)$$

An example of a weak acid is ethanoic acid. In aqueous solution it is only partially ionised – mainly molecules, few ions.

$$CH_3COOH\ (aq) \rightleftharpoons CH_3COO^-(aq) + H^+(aq)$$

To distinguish between a strong and a weak acid:

- at the same concentration the stronger acid will have the lower pH
- at the same concentration the stronger acid will be the better conductor of electricity
- at the same concentration and temperature the stronger acid will react faster with solids – such as magnesium ribbon or a lump of calcium carbonate.

Examiner's tip
▶ For a fair comparison, acids must be at the same concentration and, for a reaction involving rates, at the same temperature as well as the same concentration. You must make the comparison clear – just writing that a strong acid has a low pH would not be awarded a mark.

Strong and weak bases

Examples of strong bases are sodium hydroxide and potassium hydroxide. In aqueous solution these are completely ionised – all separate ions.

$$NaOH(aq) \rightarrow Na^+(aq) + OH^-(aq)$$

An example of a weak base is ammonia. In aqueous solution it is only partially ionised – mainly molecules, few ions.

$$NH_3(aq) + H_2O(l) \rightleftharpoons OH^-(aq) + NH_4^+(aq)$$

To distinguish between a strong and a weak base:

- at the same concentration the stronger base will have the higher pH
- at the same concentration the stronger base will be the better conductor of electricity.

Acidity in soil

The prolonged use of ammonium fertilisers, acid rain or the rotting of vegetation can produce acidic soils. Some plants prefer the pH of the soil to be about 7, that is neutral. The acidity can be removed by adding crushed limestone.

$$CaCO_3(s) + 2H^+(aq) \rightarrow Ca^{2+}(aq) + CO_2(g) + H_2O(l)$$

Calcium oxide and calcium hydroxide are also used, but as they are soluble in water an excess will make the soil alkaline. This does not arise with limestone which is insoluble in water – it can be added in excess without making the soil alkaline.

Types of oxide

Basic oxides react with acids to form a salt and water. Most metal oxides are basic.

$$MgO(s) + 2HCl(aq) \rightarrow MgCl_2(aq) + H_2O(l)$$
white $\qquad$ colourless

A few metal oxides are soluble in water. These are alkalis and will turn red litmus blue.

Acidic oxides react with alkalis to form salts. Some will react with water to form an acid. These will turn blue litmus red. Acidic oxides are the oxides of non-metals – sulphur dioxide, sulphur trioxide, carbon dioxide and the oxides of phosphorus.

$$SO_3 + H_2O \rightarrow H_2SO_4$$

$$CO_2 + 2NaOH \rightarrow Na_2CO_3 + H_2O$$

$$CaO + SiO_2 \rightarrow CaSiO_3$$
base $\quad$ acid

Neutral oxides do not react with acids or bases. Examples are water, nitrogen(II) oxide and carbon monoxide.

Amphoteric oxides react with either a base or an acid to form a salt and water. They show the properties of both a base and an acid. Examples are zinc oxide and aluminium oxide. The hydroxides of the same metals behave in the same way.

Behaving as a base $\quad ZnO + 2HNO_3 \rightarrow Zn(NO_3)_2 + H_2O$

$$Al_2O_3 + 6HCl \rightarrow 2AlCl_3 + 3H_2O$$

$$Zn(OH)_2 + 2HNO_3 \rightarrow Zn(NO_3)_2 + 2H_2O$$

$$Al(OH)_3 + 3HCl \rightarrow AlCl_3 + 3H_2O$$

● **Behaving as an acid**

$$ZnO + 2NaOH \rightarrow Na_2ZnO_2 + H_2O$$
$$\text{sodium zincate}$$

$$Al_2O_3 + 2NaOH \rightarrow 2NaAlO_2 + H_2O$$
$$\text{sodium aluminate}$$

$$Zn(OH)_2 + 2NaOH \rightarrow Na_2ZnO_2 + 2H_2O$$

$$Al(OH)_3 + NaOH \rightarrow NaAlO_2 + 2H_2O$$

> **Examiner's tip**
> ▶ You will have to learn these equations – there is no easy way of working them out.

Sample questions and answers

Sample question 1   Describe two ways you could show that propanoic acid is a weaker acid than hydrobromic acid. You are given $0.1\,mol/dm^3$ solutions of both acids.   [4 marks]

> **Examiner's tip**
> ▶ Even when the acids are unfamiliar the principle remains the same. Describe the tests and give the results for both acids.

Model answer   Measure the pH of both solutions by adding universal indicator. ✓ Propanoic acid will have a higher pH than hydrobromic acid, ✓ showing that it is the weaker acid. Measure the electrical conductivity of each. ✓ Propanoic acid will be a poorer ✓ conductor than hydrobromic acid.

Examiner's comment   *'Propanoic acid will have a pH = 3' would not gain the mark, since there is no comparison with hydrobromic acid.*

Sample question 2   Complete the table which summarises the reaction of each different type of oxide with a strong acid and an alkali. The first line has been done as an example.   [6 marks]

Model answer

Type of oxide and example	Reaction with hydrochloric acid	Reaction with aqueous sodium hydroxide
basic, copper(II) oxide	reacts	no reaction
acidic, silicon(IV) oxide	no reaction ✓	reaction ✓
neutral, carbon monoxide	no reaction ✓	no reaction ✓
amphoteric, zinc oxide	reacts ✓	reacts ✓

● **Try this** *The answers are given on pp. 122–3.*

1 Match the pH values to the descriptions.

1, 5, 7, 11, 13

weakly alkaline, neutral, strongly acidic, strongly alkaline, weakly acidic

[5 marks]

Examiner's tip

► If the equation is given in words, complete it as a word equation. Similarly, if the equation is given using formulae, complete it as a symbol equation.

2 Complete the following equations.

zinc carbonate + nitric acid → . . . .

$Ca(OH)_2 + 2HCl →$ . . . .

$ZnO + 2H^+ →$ . . . .

. . . . → lithium chloride + hydrogen

$Mg(OH)_2 + H_2SO_4 →$ . . . .

$NH_4NO_3 + NaOH →$ . . . .   [6 marks]

3 Chloric(VII) acid is a typical strong acid. It forms salts called chlorate(VII). The valency of the chlorate(VII) group is one.
   a) Complete the following.
       i) zinc + chloric(VII) acid →
      ii) potassium hydroxide + chloric(VII) acid →
     iii) $Mg + HClO_4 →$
      iv) $Mg(OH)_2 + HClO_4 →$
       v) $Na_2CO_3 + HClO_4 →$
      vi) $ZnO + HClO_4 →$
     vii) $CaCO_3 + HClO_4 →$ [14 marks]
   b) Write the ionic equation for the reaction between chloric(VII) acid and the strong base sodium hydroxide.   [1 mark]
   c) Describe how you could show using magnesium ribbon that chloric(VII) acid is a stronger acid than ethanoic acid. State how you would ensure that the comparison between these two acids is a fair one.   [6 marks]

4 Sodium hydrogencarbonate, sodium carbonate and sodium hydroxide are all soluble bases. Sodium hydrogencarbonate is the weakest and sodium hydroxide the strongest. The pH of 0.1 mol/dm³ solutions of each was measured.
   a) What would these pH values have in common?   [1 mark]
   b) How would they differ?   [2 marks]

5 The fish and vegetation in a lake were dying. The pH of the lake was far too low. What was the probable cause of the low pH?

Which of these two bases, calcium oxide or calcium carbonate, should be added to the lake to bring the pH back to about 7? Explain your choice.   [4 marks]

TOPIC 13 Preparation of salts

Key objectives

- To be able to describe the preparation and purification of soluble salts
- To be able to describe the preparation of insoluble salts by precipitation
- To be able to suggest a method of making a salt from a given starting material

Key ideas

Methods of preparing soluble salts

Titration

This is used to prepare a soluble salt from a soluble base, such as sodium hydroxide or sodium carbonate, and an acid. This method is used to make salts of the Group I metals and ammonium salts.

Neutralisation of an insoluble base by an acid

An excess of the base is added to an acid, and the excess of the base is removed by filtration. The filtrate is partially evaporated to obtain crystals of the salt. Soluble salts of most of the other metals are made by this method.

Metal reacting with acid

This method is essentially the same as the one above. The reaction is not neutralisation but redox. The method can be used to make magnesium, zinc, aluminium and iron(II) salts. It cannot be used to prepare salts of very reactive metals, such as sodium and potassium, because the reaction would be too violent.

Preparation of insoluble compounds by precipitation

Insoluble compounds are:

- all carbonates except those of the Group I metals and ammonium carbonate
- all hydroxides except those of the Group I metals and those of calcium, strontium and barium
- barium, calcium and lead sulphates
- the chlorides, bromides and iodides, of both silver and lead.

To make the insoluble salt barium sulphate, two solutions are mixed. One solution contains a soluble barium salt and the other a soluble sulphate. The precipitate of barium sulphate is filtered off, washed and dried.

$$BaCl_2(aq) + Na_2SO_4(aq) \rightarrow BaSO_4(s) + 2NaCl(aq)$$

$$Ba^{2+}(aq) + SO_4^{2-}(aq) \rightarrow BaSO_4(s)$$

● **Try this** *The answers are given on p. 123.*

1 Hydrated nickel sulphate crystals can be made by adding an *excess* of nickel carbonate to 25 cm³ of dilute sulphuric acid. The mixture is heated until the reaction is complete. The mixture is *filtered* and the filtrate is *partially* evaporated. It is left to cool and the crystals are filtered off and *pressed between sheets of filter paper.*

   a) Why must an excess of nickel carbonate be used?
   b) Why is the mixture filtered?
   c) Suggest a reason why the filtrate is only partially evaporated.
   d) Why are the crystals pressed between sheets of filter paper? [4 marks]

Examiner's tip
▶ You must find out if the salt is soluble or insoluble in water. If it is insoluble it has to be made by precipitation. If it is soluble, it is made from an acid.

2 Give the reagents needed to prepare each of the following salts.
   i) silver(I) bromide
   ii) copper(II) nitrate
   iii) potassium sulphate
   iv) calcium sulphate
   v) zinc chloride
   vi) lithium chloride   [12 marks]

3 The following is a description of the preparation of potassium sulphate from aqueous potassium carbonate and dilute sulphuric acid. The instructions for this preparation are given in the wrong order. Rearrange them in the correct order.

   A Partially evaporate the solution and allow it to cool.
   B Repeat the experiment using the same volumes of acid and carbonate but do not add methyl orange.
   C Fill a burette with dilute sulphuric acid and measure 25.0 cm³ of aqueous potassium carbonate into a flask.
   D Filter to obtain crystals and dry them between filter paper.
   E Record the volume of sulphuric acid needed to neutralise the carbonate.
   F Add the acid slowly from the burette until the methyl orange just changes from yellow to red.
   G Add a few drops of the indicator, methyl orange, to the aqueous potassium carbonate.   [3 marks]

4 Copy and complete this description of the preparation of the insoluble salt lead sulphate. Write one word in each space.

   Solutions of lead nitrate and sodium .... are mixed. A white .... of lead sulphate is formed. The mixture is .... The residue is washed with water to remove traces of .... salts. Finally the solid is .... to remove any water.   [5 marks]

TOPIC 14 Identification of ions and gases

Key objectives
- To be able to recall the tests used to identify the specified cations
- To be able to recall the tests used to identify the specified anions
- To describe suitable tests to identify named compounds
- To be able to recall the tests used to identify the specified gases

Key ideas Tests for cations

	Test	
	Add a few drops of sodium hydroxide, then excess	Add a few drops of aqueous ammonia, then excess
Cation	**Result**	
Aluminium Al^{3+}	White precipitate, dissolves in excess forming a colourless solution	White precipitate, insoluble in excess
Ammonium NH_4^+	Ammonia gas given off on warming, turns damp red litmus paper blue	—
Calcium Ca^{2+}	White precipitate, insoluble in excess	No precipitate or very faint white precipitate
Copper Cu^{2+}	Light blue precipitate, insoluble in excess	Light blue precipitate, dissolves in excess to give a deep blue solution
Iron(II) Fe^{2+}	Green precipitate, insoluble in excess	Green precipitate, insoluble in excess
Iron(III) Fe^{3+}	Brown precipitate, insoluble in excess	Brown precipitate, insoluble in excess
Zinc Zn^{2+}	White precipitate, dissolves in excess to give a colourless solution	White precipitate, dissolves in excess to give a colourless solution

Tests for anions

Anion	Test	Result
Carbonate CO_3^{2-} aqueous or solid	Add dilute hydrochloric acid	Effervescence, carbon dioxide given off, limewater goes milky
Chloride Cl^- aqueous only	Add excess dilute nitric acid and then aqueous silver nitrate	White precipitate
Iodide I^- aqueous only	Add excess dilute nitric acid and then aqueous silver nitrate	Bright yellow precipitate
Iodide I^- aqueous only	Add excess dilute nitric acid and then aqueous lead(II) nitrate	Yellow precipitate
Nitrate NO_3^- aqueous only	Warm with aqueous sodium hydroxide and aluminium foil	Ammonia given off, pungent smell, turns red litmus paper blue
Sulphate SO_4^{2-} aqueous only	Add excess hydrochloric acid and aqueous barium chloride	White precipitate

Tests for gases

Gas	Test and result
Ammonia NH_3	Turns damp red litmus paper blue
Carbon dioxide CO_2	Turns limewater milky
Chlorine Cl_2	Bleaches damp litmus paper
Hydrogen H_2	When mixed with air, goes 'pop' with a lighted splint
Oxygen O_2	Relights a glowing splint

Examiner's tips

▶ You will have to learn these tests. Hopefully practical work should make this process fairly easy.
▶ The most common type of question asks you to describe a test. You must always give the reagent or details of the test and the result.
▶ If you are asked, for example, how an aluminium salt reacts with aqueous sodium hydroxide, you need to answer in this way:

- with the addition of aqueous sodium hydroxide, a white precipitate forms
- with the addition of excess sodium hydroxide, the precipitate dissolves to give a colourless solution.

DO NOT:
- write that the solution 'goes white'
- think that 'clear' and 'colourless' have the same meaning
- mix up the result of adding a few drops with the result of adding excess sodium hydroxide – write two separate sentences.

Common error

A candidate was asked to describe the test for a chloride and wrote:
    'Add an excess of hydrochloric acid to a solution of the suspected chloride. Now add silver nitrate solution, if a chloride is present a white precipitate will form.'
    No marks were awarded. Hydrochloric acid is a chloride, so a white precipitate will form every time. ■

Identifying a compound

Sample question   A salt gave a white precipitate which dissolved in excess with both sodium hydroxide and aqueous ammonia. A solution of this salt gave a white precipitate with acidified barium chloride solution. Identify the salt.   [2 marks]

Student's answer   It is zinc sulphate.

Examiner's comment   *Check this yourself by looking at the tables of tests. The marked question with examiner's comments is on p. 123.*

TOPIC 15 The periodic table: periodic trends

Key objectives

- To know how the elements are arranged in the periodic table
- To be able to describe the change from metallic to non-metallic character across a period
- To know the general differences in properties between metals and non-metals
- To be able to describe the relationship between group number, number of valency electrons and metallic/non-metallic character

Key ideas

Arrangement of elements in the table

The elements are arranged in order of proton number. Elements with similar chemical properties are placed in the same vertical column. This is called a group. Elements in a group have similar chemical properties, the same outer electron distribution and usually the same valency. Going down a group, the elements become more metallic in character.

The horizontal rows are called periods. Moving across a period the elements change from metallic to non-metallic. The number of valency electrons increases across the period but the number of occupied energy levels stays the same.

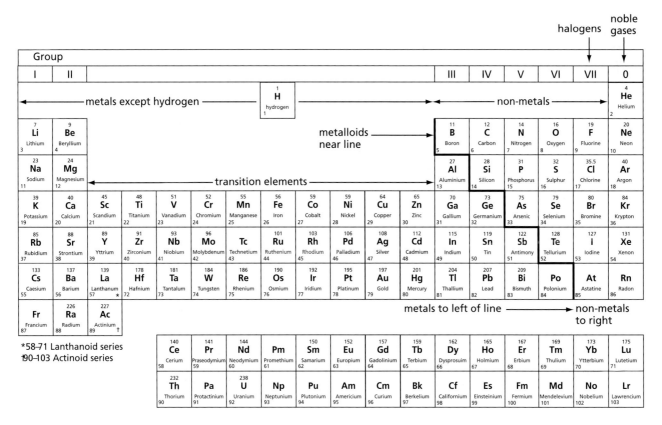

Figure 15.1 The periodic table of the elements

Differences between metals and non-metals

The following tables of differences in properties should be taken only as a guide; there are many exceptions.

● **Physical differences**

Metals	Non-metals
Usually have high melting and boiling points. Solids at room temperature Exceptions: Group I metals have low melting points and mercury is a liquid	Melting points and boiling points are low Exceptions: those non-metals with macromolecular structures –carbon, silicon, boron, germanium
Good conductors of both heat and electricity	Poor conductors Exception: graphite
Hard Exceptions: Group I metals are soft	Soft Exceptions: those non-metals with macromolecular structures –carbon, silicon, boron, germanium
High densities Exceptions: Group I metals have low densities	Low densities
Malleable (can have their shape changed by hammering) Ductile (can be pulled into wires)	Brittle (do not change shape but break) Exception: graphite
Sonorous (think of a bell)	Not sonorous
Can be polished to a lustre (shiny)	Have a dull surface Exceptions: graphite, iodine

● **Chemical differences**

Chemical property	Metals	Non-metals
Electron distribution and bonding	1, 2 or 3 valency electrons These are lost to form cations (positive ions)	4, 5, 6 or 7 valency electrons Either gain electrons to form anions (negative ions) or share electron pairs
Type of compound	Form ionic compounds with non-metals: see properties of ionic compounds in Topic 4 (p. 19)	Form covalent compounds with other non-metals: see properties of covalent compounds in Topic 4 (p. 19)
Class of oxide	Metal oxides are usually basic; a few are amphoteric: see Topic 12	Non-metal oxides are usually acidic; a few are neutral
Reaction with acids	Many react with dilute acids to give a salt and hydrogen	Do not react with acids to give a salt and hydrogen: see Topics 12 and 18

● **Try this**   *The answers are given on p. 123.*

1 Calcium and phosphorus are in the same period in the periodic table.

   a) Which one will be the better conductor of electricity? Give a reason for your choice. [2 marks]

   b) Complete the following word equations. If the substances do not react, write 'no reaction'.

   calcium + hydrochloric acid → ....

   phosphorus + hydrochloric acid → .... [3 marks]

    c) The oxides of calcium and phosphorus are both soluble in water. Describe how you could distinguish between solutions of their oxides. [3 marks]

2 Selenium is a non-metal in Group VI.
    a) Predict three physical properties of selenium. [3 marks]
    b) How many valency electrons are there in one selenium atom? [1 mark]
    c) Predict the formula of selenium chloride. [1 mark]
    d) Is selenium chloride an ionic or a covalent compound? Give a reason for your choice. [2 marks]

3 Germanium is a non-metal in Group IV.
    a) Complete the electron distribution of a germanium atom. Two numbers are missing.

        ..+ 8 + 18 + ... [2 marks]

    b) Carbon and germanium are both non-metals. They are both poor conductors of electricity. Predict which is the better conductor, giving a reason for your choice. [2 marks]
    c) Write the formula of:
        i) germanium(IV) fluoride
        ii) germanium(IV) oxide [2 marks]
    d) Describe how you could show that germanium(IV) oxide is amphoteric. [2 marks]
    e) Germanium has macromolecular structure similar to that of diamond, whereas phosphorus exists as covalent molecules. Predict two differences in the physical properties of these two non-metals. [2 marks]

4 Lanthanum, $Z = 57$, is a metal. Its valency is 3.
    a) i) How many subatomic particles are in the nucleus of a lanthanum atom?
        ii) How many neutrons are there in one atom of lanthanum?
        iii) What is the formula of a lanthanum ion? [3 marks]
    b) Write the formula of:
        i) lanthanum bromide
        ii) lanthanum oxide
        iii) lanthanum nitride. [3 marks]
    c) i) Predict three physical properties of lanthanum. [3 marks]
        ii) Predict two chemical properties of lanthanum. [2 marks]
    d) i) Write a word equation for the reaction between lanthanum and hydrochloric acid. [1 mark]
        ii) Write a balanced symbol equation for this reaction. [2 marks]

TOPIC 16 The periodic table: group properties

Key objectives

- To be able to describe the physical and chemical properties of the first three metals in Group I
- To be able to predict the properties of the other metals in Group I
- To know that reactivity of the metals increases down the group
- To be able to describe the physical and chemical properties of chlorine, bromine and iodine
- To be able to predict the properties of the other halogens
- To identify trends in other groups given the relevant information
- To understand that noble gases are unreactive
- To be able to describe the uses of helium and argon

Key ideas

Group I: the alkali metals

Atom		Electronic structure	Ion	Electronic structure
Lithium	Li	2,1	Li$^+$	2
Sodium	Na	2,8,1	Na$^+$	2,8
Potassium	K	2,8,8,1	K$^+$	2,8,8

Lithium, sodium and potassium all have a valency of one and they form ions that have the same electronic structure as the nearest noble gas.

• Physical properties

- They are all very soft metals. Lithium is the hardest of the three and potassium the softest. The Group I metals generally become softer down the group.
- They have silvery, shiny surfaces when freshly cut.
- They are all good conductors of heat and electricity.
- They all have low melting points: lithium 181 °C, sodium 98 °C and potassium 64 °C. The melting points decrease down the group.
- Their densities are very low, less than 1.0 g/cm^3. The trend in density going down the group is that there is a general increase.

  Li 0.53   Na 0.97   K 0.86   Rb 1.53   Cs 1.9 g/cm^3

The trend is spoilt by sodium and potassium being 'out of step'.

• Chemical properties

The alkali metals are the most reactive metals. Their reactivity increases down the group. They are kept under oil, otherwise they would react with the oxygen and water in the air.

They all react violently with cold water to form the hydroxide, NOT the oxide, and hydrogen.

Lithium floats and reacts steadily.

$$2Li + 2H_2O \rightarrow 2LiOH + H_2$$

Sodium melts and moves rapidly across the surface. The hydrogen does not usually ignite.

$$2Na + 2H_2O \rightarrow 2NaOH + H_2$$

Potassium melts and moves rapidly across the surface. The hydrogen ignites and there may be an explosion. Note that the reactions are becoming more violent as the metals become more reactive.

$$2K + 2H_2O \rightarrow 2KOH + H_2$$

Group VII: the halogens

Halogen		Electron structure	Ion	Electron structure	Molecular formula	State at r.t.p	Colour
Chlorine	Cl	2,8,7	Cl⁻	2,8,8	Cl_2	Gas	Yellow/green
Bromine	Br	2,8,18,7	Br⁻	2,8,18,8	Br_2	Liquid	Brown
Iodine	I	2,8,18,18,7	I⁻	2,8,18,18,8	I_2	Solid	Black crystals, purple vapour when heated

Chlorine, bromine and iodine are all covalent diatomic molecules: they have two atoms per molecule.

● **Physical properties**
- ● The colour gets darker down the group.
- ● The melting and boiling points increase down the group.

> **Examiner's tip**
> ▶ You do not have to learn the electron distributions for bromine and iodine, just look at the pattern for the valency electrons. They all have seven electrons in their outer level. Also note that the number of occupied levels or shells increases down the group.

● **Reaction with other elements to form halides**

Sodium will burn in chlorine to form sodium chloride.

$$2Na + Cl_2 \rightarrow 2NaCl$$

Iron will react with bromine when heated.

$$2Fe + 3Br_2 \rightarrow 2FeBr_3$$

A mixture of aluminium and iodine will react to form aluminium iodide when a drop of water is added.

$$2Al + 3I_2 \rightarrow 2AlI_3$$

● **Reactivity of halogens**

Compared with the Group I metals, the trend is reversed. The reactivity increases *up* the group. Chlorine can displace both bromine and iodine from their compounds. The reaction with a bromide is:

chlorine + potassium bromide → potassium chloride + bromine

$$Cl_2 + 2KBr \rightarrow 2KCl + Br_2$$

The colour changes to orange/brown, the colour of bromine.

71 ●

Similarly, with iodides:

$$Cl_2 + 2KI \rightarrow 2KCl + I_2$$

The colour changes to dark brown, the colour of iodine.

Bromine can displace iodine from iodides but not chlorine from chlorides.

bromine + sodium iodide $\rightarrow$ sodium bromide + iodine

$$Br_2 + 2NaI \rightarrow 2NaBr + I_2$$

These reactions are redox. For the reaction of chlorine and potassium bromide, the symbol equation is:

$$Cl_2 + 2KBr \rightarrow 2KCl + Br_2$$

The ionic equation is:

$$Cl_2 + 2Br^- \rightarrow 2Cl^- + Br_2$$

Remember OILRIG (see Topic 11, p. 54).

$$Cl_2 + 2e^- \rightarrow 2Cl^-$$

This is reduction, because chlorine molecules gain electrons.

$$2Br^- - 2e^- \rightarrow Br_2$$

This is oxidation, because bromide ions lose electrons.

Noble gases: Group 0

The noble gases are unreactive; they have a valency of 0. Their outer electron shell is complete, so they do not transfer electrons or share electron pairs. They do not form chemical bonds with other elements.

● **Uses of the noble gases**
- Helium is used in balloons: it is less dense than air and safer than hydrogen.
- A helium (80%) and oxygen (20%) mixture is used by deep sea divers.
- Liquid helium is used in low temperature research.
- Neon is used in advertising signs.
- Argon is used to fill electric light bulbs because it is inert.
- Argon is used to provide an inert atmosphere in welding.

● **Try this** *The answers are given on p. 124.*

1   Predict what you would see when rubidium reacts with water. Write an equation for the reaction.   [5 marks]

> **Examiner's tip**
> ▶ Think about the trend in reactivity in Group I. You should know what you would see when potassium reacts with water. The equation for the reaction with water follows the same pattern as for the other Group I metals.

2 Predict the melting point of rubidium from the following data. Explain your choice.

Melting points:

lithium 181 °C, sodium 98 °C, potassium 64 °C, caesium 29 °C   [2 marks]

3 Predict the following about the halogen astatine.
   a) What is its molecular formula?   [1 mark]
   b) Describe its appearance at r.t.p.   [2 marks]
   c) What is the formula for calcium astatide?   [1 mark]
   d) Which of the following pairs would react together? Give a reason for your choice.

   astatine and potassium iodide

   iodine and potassium astatide   [2 marks]

Examiner's tip
▶ Follow the pattern in the examples in the text, see p. 72.

4 **a)** Write an ionic equation for the reaction between fluorine and potassium chloride.   [2 marks]
   b) Identify the change which is reduction and the reagent which is the reducing agent.   [4 marks]

5 The noble gases are in Group 0.
   a) Argon is used to fill electric light bulbs. Inside the bulb the filament, a thin metal wire, becomes white hot. Why is an inert atmosphere essential?   [1 mark]
   b) Helium is used to fill balloons in preference to hydrogen because it is safer. Explain.   [2 marks]
   c) Most gaseous elements exist as diatomic molecules, for example O_2. The noble gases are monatomic – they exist as single atoms, for example Ne. Explain this difference.   [4 marks]
   d) Calculate the density of argon at r.t.p. in g/dm^3.   [2 marks]

6 Some of the Group II metals are :

magnesium   very slow reaction with cold water, burns in steam
calcium
strontium   all three react with cold water
barium

   a) Predict which metal is most reactive.   [1 mark]
   b) **i)** Write the word equation for the reaction between magnesium and steam.   [2 marks]
      ii) Write the equation for the reaction of calcium with cold water.   [2 marks]
      iii) Write the equation for the reaction between strontium and hydrochloric acid.   [2 marks]
   c) Give a diagram showing the arrangement of the valency electrons in the compound barium oxide.   [3 marks]

TOPIC 17 Transition elements

Key objectives

- To be able to identify a transition element from its position in the periodic table
- To be able to describe the typical characteristics of these elements
- To be able to compare transition metals with other metals, such as magnesium

Key ideas

There are three series of transition elements in the middle of the periodic table. The first series is from scandium to zinc.

Physical characteristics

Transition elements are metals with higher densities and melting points than the metals in Groups I and II. They are harder and stronger than the metals in Groups I and II.

Chemical characteristics

Transition elements are less reactive than Group I and II metals. They do not react with cold water, but many of them react when heated in steam.

$$Zn + H_2O \rightarrow ZnO + H_2$$

> **Examiner's tip**
> ▶ Remember that when a metal is heated in steam, the *oxide* is formed. Metals that react with cold water form their *hydroxides*.

Transition elements have more than one oxidation state or valency. Iron forms Fe^{2+} and Fe^{3+}, while chromium has oxidation states from +2 as in Cr^{2+} to +6 as in CrO_4^{2-}. They form coloured compounds.

- Iron(II) salts are pale green and iron(III) salts are yellow/brown.
- Copper(II) salts are blue.
- Nickel salts are bright green.

The transition elements and their compounds both behave as catalysts. Two important examples in IGCSE Chemistry are iron in the Haber process (see Topic 20) and vanadium(V) oxide in the Contact process (see Topic 21).

● Try this

The answer is given on pp. 124–5.

1   Compare the chemistry of magnesium and manganese by giving two differences in physical properties and two differences in chemical properties. [4 marks]

> **Examiner's tip**
> ▶ It is essential that each of your statements draws a clear comparison between the two metals. For example, to write that manganese has a high melting point would not gain any marks. You need to write 'manganese has a higher melting point than magnesium'.

Topic 18 Properties of metals

Key objectives
- To be able to describe the general chemical and physical properties of metals
- To be familiar with the reactivity series
- To be able to extend the reactivity series to include redox reactions and stability of compounds – nitrates and hydroxides
- To be able to deduce order of reactivity from experimental results

Key ideas
The physical properties of metals have been discussed in Topics 4 and 15. Their chemical properties will be covered throughout this topic.

Reactivity series

Metals in order of reactivity	Reaction with water or steam	Reaction with dilute hydrochloric acid	Reduction of oxide with carbon
Potassium	React violently with cold water to form the hydroxide and hydrogen	Dangerous, explosive violence	–
Sodium			–
Calcium	Reacts quickly with cold water	Very vigorous reaction to form the chloride and hydrogen	–
Magnesium	Very slowly with cold water but burns in steam to form its oxide	Very vigorous reaction to form the chloride and hydrogen	Metal oxides above zinc cannot be reduced with carbon
Zinc	React when heated in steam to form the oxide and hydrogen	React to form the chloride and hydrogen	Zinc oxide can be reduced to zinc by heating with carbon
Iron	Do not react with cold water		All metal oxides below zinc can be reduced with carbon to form the metal
*Hydrogen			
Copper	Does not react with cold water or steam	Metals below hydrogen do not react with dilute acid	Reduced to copper

* The non-metal hydrogen is included in the first column of the table to show that metals above it react with dilute acid to form a salt and hydrogen, whereas metals below it do not react with dilute acid

Stability of compounds

The more reactive the metal, the more stable its compounds.

Most metal hydroxides decompose when heated, to give the oxide and water.

$$Zn(OH)_2 \rightarrow ZnO + H_2O$$

Sodium and potassium hydroxides do not decompose when heated.

All nitrates decompose when heated. Sodium and potassium nitrates decompose to the nitrite and oxygen.

$$2NaNO_3 \rightarrow 2NaNO_2 + O_2$$

Nitrates of less reactive metals decompose further, that is to the oxide, nitrogen dioxide and oxygen.

$$2Mg(NO_3)_2 \rightarrow 2MgO + 4NO_2 + O_2$$

Examiner's tip
▶ You need to learn these equations, as they are very difficult to work out.

75

Sample questions and answers

Sample question 1 To compare the reactivities of tin and mercury, a clean piece of tin was placed in aqueous mercury(II) chloride. After a few minutes a silvery deposit was seen on the tin. This showed that tin was more reactive than mercury. The experiment was repeated with other metals and their salts. The results are shown below.

Solution	Tin	Scandium	Mercury	Iron
Tin(II) chloride		Reaction	No reaction	Reaction
Scandium chloride	No reaction		No reaction	No reaction
Mercury(II) chloride	Reaction	Reaction		Reaction
Iron(II) sulphate	No reaction	Reaction	No reaction	

a) What is the order of reactivity of these four metals? Write the most reactive first and the least reactive last. [2 marks]

Student's answer Scandium ✓, tin ✗, iron, mercury.

Examiner's comment *The first and last are correct (1 mark) but iron can displace tin, so iron should be second.*

Model answer Scandium ✓, iron, tin ✓, mercury.

b) The reactivity series can be written as a series of ionic equations.

$$Sc \rightarrow Sc^{3+} + 3e^-$$ *(Remember all the atoms are reducing agents;*
$$Fe \rightarrow Fe^{2+} + 2e^-$$ *they can lose electrons to an oxidising agent.*
$$Sn \rightarrow Sn^{2+} + 2e^-$$ *Remember all the ions are oxidising agents;*
$$Hg \rightarrow Hg^{2+} + 2e^-$$ *they can accept electrons.)*

i) Which metal in the list has the greatest tendency to form its positive ion? [1 mark]

Student's answer Scandium ✓

Examiner's comment *Good answer, it is the most reactive so it has the greatest tendency to lose electrons and form positive ions.*

ii) Which ion is the best oxidising agent? [1 mark]

Student's answer Scandium ion ✗

Examiner's comments *Wrong. This is a bit confusing, as scandium metal is the best reducing agent and mercury the worst. The mercury ion is the best oxidising agent and the scandium ion the worst. Remember – the scandium is the best at losing electrons so it follows that the scandium ion must be the poorest at accepting them.*

Model answer Mercury ion ✓

iii) Which ions can be reduced by iron metal? [2 marks]

Student's answer Tin ✓ and mercury ✓ ions.

Examiner's comment   *Good. This is just a different way of asking which metals can be displaced by iron.*

Sample question 2   The simple cell in Figure 18.1 was set up and the voltage measured.

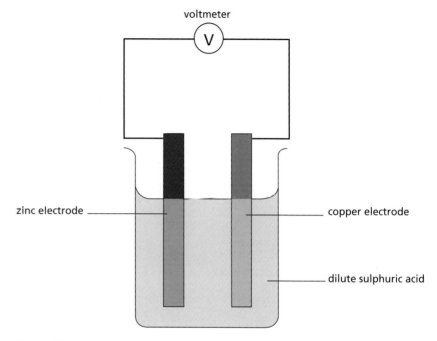

Figure 18.1

The zinc electrode was replaced by different metals and the voltages of these cells were measured.

Positive electrode	Negative electrode	Voltage/volts
copper	zinc	1.1
copper	tin	0.48
copper	iron	0.78
silver	copper	0.46
copper	magnesium	2.7

a) Explain why the more reactive metal is always the negative electrode. [2 marks]

Student's answer   The metal higher in the reactivity series is the negative electrode. ✗

Examiner's comment   *The answer is a true statement but it does not answer the question. It merely rephrases information given in the question.*

Model answer   The more reactive metal has the greater tendency to lose electrons and form ions. ✓ The ions go into solution and the electrons move in the wire away from this electrode. This electrode has to be negative ✓ and the less reactive metal is the positive electrode.

> **Examiner's tip**
> ▶ Think of the direction of electron flow. As electrons are negatively charged, they will move through the external circuit from the negative to the positive electrode.

b) The order of reactivity is – magnesium, zinc, iron, tin, copper, silver.

  i) How do you know, from the information given in the question, that copper is above silver in the series?   [1 mark]

Student's answer   Because it has the smallest voltage. ✗

Model answer   Because in the copper/silver cell, copper is the negative electrode and silver the positive. ✓ This shows that copper is more reactive than silver.

Examiner's comment   *It is just chance that it has the lowest voltage.*

  ii) How can you establish the order of reactivity of zinc, iron and magnesium? They are all more reactive than copper. [2 marks]

Student's answer   Put them in the order of the voltage of the cells. ✓ The bigger the voltage, the bigger the difference in reactivity. ✓

Examiner's comment   *A perfect answer, the first comment answers the question and the second one would ensure full marks.*

  iii) Using the metals in the question, which cell would produce the highest voltage?   [2 marks]

Student's answer   The cell with the highest voltage would be a magnesium ✓/ silver ✓ cell.

Examiner's comment   *The student has correctly paired the most reactive metal with the least reactive, to get the biggest difference in reactivity.*

TOPIC 19 Extraction and uses of metals

Key objectives

- To relate the ease of extracting a metal from its ore to the position of the metal in the reactivity series
- To be able to describe the essential features of the extraction of iron from haematite
- To be able to describe the conversion of iron into steel
- To be able to describe some of the different types of steel and their uses
- To be able to describe the extraction of zinc from zinc blende
- To be able to name the uses of zinc as galvanising and making alloys
- To be able to explain why metals are used in the form of alloys rather than the pure metal
- To relate the uses of copper to its properties
- To relate the uses of aluminium to its properties

Key ideas

Extraction of metals from their ores

The general principle was discussed in Topic 18 – the more reactive a metal, the more stable its compounds. The most reactive metals – potassium, sodium, calcium, magnesium and aluminium – are extracted from their ores by electrolysis of a molten compound. Refer to Topic 7 for the extraction of aluminium.

For zinc and all less reactive metals, a chemical reducing agent can be used, typically carbon or carbon monoxide.

The least reactive metal, gold, is found 'native', that is as the metal not as a compound.

Details of the extraction of zinc

- The ore is zinc blende, ZnS.
- This is roasted in air to form the oxide.

$$2ZnS + 3O_2 \rightarrow 2ZnO + 2SO_2$$

- The oxide is heated with carbon in a furnace, where it is reduced to zinc.

$$ZnO + C \rightarrow Zn + CO \quad \text{or} \quad 2ZnO + C \rightarrow 2Zn + CO_2$$

- Zinc distils out of the furnace.

Extraction of iron: the chemistry of the blast furnace

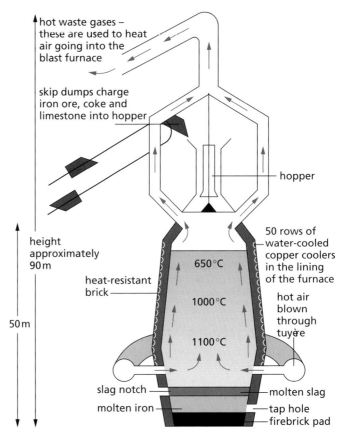

Figure 19.1 Cross-section through a blast furnace

Labels in figure:
- hot waste gases – these are used to heat air going into the blast furnace
- skip dumps charge iron ore, coke and limestone into hopper
- hopper
- height approximately 90 m
- 50 m
- heat-resistant brick
- 650 °C
- 1000 °C
- 1100 °C
- 50 rows of water-cooled copper coolers in the lining of the furnace
- hot air blown through tuyère
- slag notch
- molten iron
- molten slag
- tap hole
- firebrick pad

Examiner's tip
▶ You do not need to learn the diagram of the blast furnace but you need to know the general set-up. You may be asked to label a diagram of the blast furnace, or to answer questions of the type, 'Where is the iron tapped off?' Questions will be confined to the essential reactions and a general understanding of the process.

Haematite (iron ore), together with coke and limestone, are added at the top of the furnace (Figure 19.1). Hot air is blown into the furnace. The coke burns, producing large amounts of heat.

$$C + O_2 \rightarrow CO_2$$

The limestone decomposes.

$$CaCO_3 \rightarrow CaO + CO_2$$

Higher up the furnace, the oxygen has been used up and the carbon dioxide is reduced to carbon monoxide.

$$CO_2 + C \rightarrow 2CO$$

This reduces the ore, iron(III) oxide, to iron, which flows down to the bottom of the furnace.

$$Fe_2O_3 + 3CO \rightarrow 2Fe + 3CO_2$$

An impurity in the ore is sand, silicon(IV) oxide. This reacts with calcium oxide to form slag. The molten slag runs to the bottom of the furnace and floats on the molten iron. It can be run off separately and used as a building material.

calcium oxide + silicon(IV) oxide → calcium silicate (slag)

$$CaO + SiO_2 \rightarrow CaSiO_3$$

Examiner's tip
▶ This reaction is a good example of a basic oxide, CaO, reacting with an acidic oxide, SiO_2, to form a salt, $CaSiO_3$.

Uses of metals

- Zinc: making alloys such as brass, galvanising (see Topic 20).
- Aluminium: aircraft construction, because it has low density, food containers and cooking foil, because it is resistant to corrosion.

   Aluminium is between magnesium and zinc in the reactivity series so it ought to be a reactive metal, but it is protected from chemical attack by an adherent layer of its oxide. It behaves as an unreactive metal because of this oxide layer.
- Copper: electrical wiring, because it is an excellent conductor of electricity and is ductile so it can be pulled into wires; and cooking utensils, because it is a good conductor of heat and is malleable (easily shaped).

> ### Examiner's tip
> ▶ The uses given in this section are those specified in the syllabus. You can probably think of many more uses –copper piping, aluminium window frames, copper and zinc for roofing, zinc electrodes, etc. Any correct use would be awarded a mark.

Alloys

An alloy is a mixture of two or more metals, or a mixture of one or more metals with a non-metal. Alloys are used in preference to the pure metal because they can be designed to have properties better suited for a particular use, for example they may be harder, more resistant to corrosion, or have a more attractive appearance.

   The structure of a typical alloy is shown in Figure 19.2. It is likely to be harder than the pure metal (dark circles) because the presence of a different sized atom will prevent the layers from slipping.

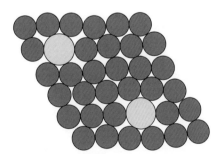

Figure 19.2 Structure of a typical alloy. The dark circles represent atoms of a metal; the paler circles are the larger atoms of a different metal added to make the alloy

Examples of alloys
- Brass: a mixture of zinc and copper.
- Mild steel: up to about 0.3% carbon; used for car bodies and machinery.
- Stainless steel: iron, nickel and chromium; used for chemical plant and cutlery. It is very resistant to corrosion.

Sample questions and answers

Sample question 1 **a)** Why must limestone be added to the blast furnace?   [2 marks]

Student's answer It removes the sand, ✓ which is in the ore, as slag. ✓

Examiner's comments *A good answer, much better than the simple comment, 'It removes sand'. A less obvious reason is that the slag that is formed separates the molten iron from the oxygen in the air. If it did not, the hot iron would react with oxygen to re-form iron oxide.*

b) Name the substances that leave the blast furnace.   [4 marks]

Student's answer (Molten) iron, ✓ (molten) slag ✓ and the oxides of carbon. ✓

Examiner's comments *One substance missing — nitrogen (from the air). The information given in brackets would not generally be needed for the marks.*

Sample question 2 The impure iron from the blast furnace contains about 5% impurities, such as carbon, sulphur, silicon and phosphorus. Describe how the impure iron is converted into steel, typically 0.1% carbon.   [6 marks]

Student's answer Oxygen is blown through the molten iron. ✓ The impurities are oxidised and form a slag.

Examiner's comments *This is a typical example of an answer that includes correct information but lacks sufficient detail to be worth more than 1 mark. The clues are in the question — the amount of detail given invites a more detailed response, as does the award of 6 marks.*

Model answer Oxygen is blown through the molten iron. ✓ The impurities are oxidised to carbon dioxide, sulphur dioxide, silicon(IV) oxide and phosphorus oxide. ✓ ✓ The first two are gases and escape. ✓ Calcium oxide ✓ is added; this reacts with the other two oxides to form a slag. ✓ The required amount of carbon is added.

Common error

The situation in Sample question 2 is similar to the blast furnace and a very common mistake is to confuse the two processes. The blast furnace is about reducing iron(III) oxide to iron. Steel making is concerned with the removal of impurities from impure iron and controlling the percentage of carbon. ■

TOPIC 20 Air and water

Key objectives

- To be able describe a chemical test for water
- To be able to describe, in outline, the treatment of the water supply
- To be able to name some domestic and industrial uses of water
- To be able to describe the composition of unpolluted air
- To be able to name the common pollutants in air
- To know the source of these pollutants
- To be able to state the adverse effect of these pollutants on health and the environment
- To explain the presence of the oxides of nitrogen in vehicle exhausts and their removal by catalytic converters
- To be able to describe the separation of oxygen and nitrogen from liquid air by fractional distillation
- To know the uses of oxygen
- To be able to describe the methods of rust prevention by paint and other coatings which exclude oxygen and water
- To understand sacrificial protection and galvanising as methods of rust prevention
- To be able to describe the manufacture of ammonia by the Haber process
- To explain the need for NPK fertilisers
- To be able to describe the displacement of the weak base, ammonia, from its salts
- To be able to describe the formation of carbon dioxide by complete combustion, from respiration and from a carbonate and acid

Key ideas

Chemical tests for water

Water will turn anhydrous copper(II) sulphate from white to blue.

$$CuSO_4(s) + 5H_2O(l) \rightarrow CuSO_4.5H_2O$$
$$\text{white} \qquad\qquad\qquad \text{blue}$$

Water will turn anhydrous cobalt chloride from blue to pink. This test can be carried out using cobalt chloride paper.

$$CoCl_2(s) + 6H_2O(l) \rightarrow CoCl_2.6H_2O(s)$$
$$\text{blue} \qquad\qquad\qquad \text{pink}$$

These tests show only that water is present, not that a liquid is pure water.

Water treatment

Water from the reservoir is:

- filtered (through sand and gravel filters) to remove undissolved solids
- treated with chlorine to kill micro-organisms such as bacteria
- supplied to the consumer – it is safe to drink, although not pure.

Examiner's tip
▶ The complete water treatment process is complex; you only need to know the simple version given here.

Examiner's tip

▶ Some books describe the water treatment process as purification. This is incorrect – you can hardly purify water by dissolving chlorine in it.

● **Try this** *The answers are given on p. 125.*

1 How could you show that a liquid is pure water? [2 marks]

2 State three domestic uses of water and three industrial uses. [6 marks]

Air

The composition of air is 79% nitrogen, 20% oxygen, and the rest a mixture of carbon dioxide, water vapour and the noble gases.

● **Try this** *The answer is given on p. 125.*

3 The table lists four of the common atmospheric pollutants. Copy the table and complete the last row.

Pollutant	Source	Adverse effects	Action to reduce amount of pollutant
Carbon monoxide	Incomplete combustion of carbon-based fuels	Health hazard: prevents blood from transporting oxygen	Use a catalytic converter
Sulphur dioxide	Burning fossil fuels that contain sulphur	Acid rain, causing deforestation and damage to buildings	Use low-sulphur fuels or remove sulphur dioxide from flue gases with crushed limestone
Oxides of nitrogen	Oxygen and nitrogen, which react at high temperatures in car engines	Health hazard: causes severe respiratory problems; acid rain	Use a catalytic converter
Lead compounds			

[3 marks]

Catalytic converters

Oxygen and nitrogen in the air react together at the very high temperatures inside an internal petroleum engine to form the oxides of nitrogen.

$$N_2 + O_2 \rightarrow 2NO$$

$$2NO + O_2 \rightarrow 2NO_2$$

The oxides of nitrogen, carbon monoxide and unburnt hydrocarbons are all pollutants produced by motor vehicles.

Inside the catalytic converter, the following overall reactions are catalysed.

$$2NO + 2CO \rightarrow 2CO_2 + N_2$$

$$2NO_2 + 4CO \rightarrow 4CO_2 + N_2$$

Unburnt hydrocarbons are oxidised to carbon dioxide and water. The three pollutants are removed. Nitrogen and carbon dioxide, which are relatively harmless, leave the exhaust.

Oxygen

Sample question 1 Oxygen is obtained from liquid air.

a) Name the technique used to separate liquid air into oxygen and nitrogen. [1 mark]

Student's answer Fractional distillation. ✓

Examiner's comment *Good. 'Distillation' alone would not gain the mark – the word 'fractional' is essential.*

b) Explain why the technique you have given in part (a) works. [2 marks]

Student's answer Because of their boiling points. ✗

Examiner's comment *The response is not sufficiently precise.*

Model answer Because they have different boiling points: ✓ liquid nitrogen has the lower boiling point and boils off first, then the liquid oxygen boils. ✓

c) State two uses of oxygen. [2 marks]

Student's answer In hospitals for oxygen tents ✓ and welding with ethyne (acetylene). ✓

Examiner's comment *Two correct uses, gaining 2 marks.*

Examiner's tips
▶ The uses of oxygen can be divided into three types:
- medical uses – incubators, with anaesthetics, to support respiration in very sick patients
- artificial atmospheres – diving, in space, breathing apparatus for fire fighters
- general uses – cutting and welding metals, rocket fuel, re-oxygenating polluted water, making steel.

▶ Try to avoid two uses of the same type.

Common error

A very common mistake is to offer 'breathing'; this is wrong. A *use* implies that a chemical is sold for that purpose. Divers buy cylinders of oxygen for use underwater but they do not buy air to breathe. ■

Rusting
- Only iron and steel can rust; other metals corrode.
- Both water and oxygen must be present for rusting to occur.
- The rate of rusting is greatly increased by the presence of electrolytes – salt and acid rain.
- Rust is hydrated iron(III) oxide, $Fe_2O_3.xH_2O$. The amount of water in rust varies with conditions.
- Rusting is a redox reaction. The change Fe(0) to Fe(+3) is oxidation.

Methods of rust prevention involve coating the iron or steel, and so preventing contact with oxygen and/or water. This can be done by:

- painting – for example cars, ships, bridges
- using oil or grease – moving parts of machinery have to be lubricated, and this also provides a protective coating
- coating with plastic – for example freezers, fence netting, garden furniture
- plating – cans for food are plated with tin, and taps and bicycle parts can be chromium plated which both protects the steel and provides an attractive finish
- galvanising – this is coating with zinc, and has the great advantage that it provides sacrificial protection (see below).

Using stainless steel is a very expensive but effective way of preventing rusting.

Sacrificial protection

Galvanised steel is steel coated with the more reactive metal, zinc. Initially the layer of zinc prevents any contact of the inner steel with oxygen and water. When the zinc layer is broken, the exposed steel still does not rust. The more reactive metal, zinc, forms ions more readily, and electrons flow through it to the iron. This attracts hydrogen ions from the water and hydrogen gas is given off. The zinc is oxidised, but the iron is not.

The zinc loses electrons – it is oxidised (OILRIG).

The iron accepts electrons on to its surface – it does not lose electrons so it is not oxidised.

The more reactive metal does not need to coat the steel completely, but it does need to be in electrical contact. Large steel structures such as pipelines, piers and ships can be protected from corrosion by attaching bars of zinc or magnesium to them (Figure 20.1).

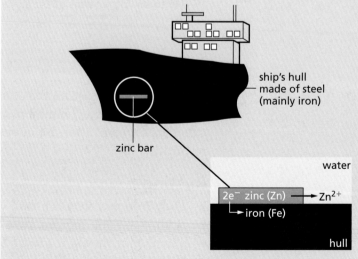

Figure 20.1 The zinc is sacrificed to protect the steel

●●

● **Try this**   *The answers are given on p. 125.*

4   Figure 20.2 shows an experiment to investigate rusting.

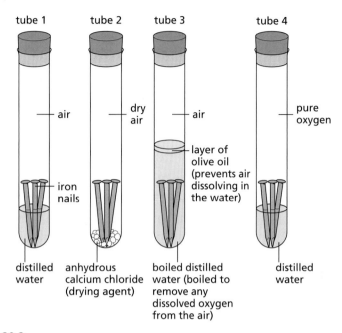

Figure 20.2

For each tube, predict whether the nails would rust. Give a reason for each of your answers.   [4 marks]

The Haber process

Ammonia is manufactured from nitrogen and hydrogen.

$$N_2(g) + 3H_2 \rightleftharpoons 2NH_3(g)$$ Forward reaction is exothermic.

Most of the ammonia is used to make fertilisers.

Nitrogen is obtained from the air. Hydrogen is made from methane, natural gas.

$$CH_4 + H_2O \rightarrow 3H_2 + CO$$

$$CO + H_2O \rightarrow H_2 + CO_2$$

Sample questions and answers

> **Examiner's tip**
> ▶ Questions are frequently set on the reaction conditions for the Haber process. You must know the conditions and be able to explain why they are used. The word 'yield' is often used; this is the percentage of ammonia in the equilibrium mixture.

Sample question 2   In the Haber process, why are nitrogen and hydrogen mixed in the ratio $1:3$ by volume?   [1 mark]

Student's answer   This is the volume or mole ratio in the reaction equation. ✓

Examiner's comment   *Yes. It is an obvious comment but needs to be stated clearly.*

Sample question 3   The catalyst in the Haber process is finely divided iron powder. What is meant by the term catalyst, and why is the catalyst finely powdered?   [3 marks]

Student's answer   A catalyst increases the rate of reaction, ✓ and finely powdered iron has a bigger surface area. ✓

Examiner's comment   *The answer could do with a little more detail for full marks.*

Model answer   A catalyst increases the rate of reaction ✓ and remains chemically unchanged. ✓ Finely powdered iron has a bigger surface area exposed to catalyse the reaction. ✓

Sample question 4   The graph in Figure 20.3 shows how the yield of ammonia varies with reaction conditions in the Haber process.

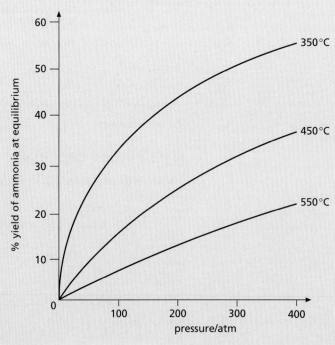

Figure 20.3

a) How and why does the yield vary with an increase in pressure?   [2 marks]

Student's answer   The yield increases when the pressure is increased. ✓ An increase in pressure favours the side of the equation with fewer gas molecules, that is the right hand side. ✓

Examiner's comment   *A model answer. In practice a pressure of about 200 atmospheres is used; higher pressures would be too expensive in engineering costs. An extra advantage of using a high pressure is faster reaction rate.*

b) How and why does the yield vary with temperature?   [2 marks]

Student's answer   An increase in temperature will favour the endothermic reaction. ✓

Examiner's comment   *The answer needs to be expanded to be awarded all the marks available.*

Model answer   An increase in temperature will favour the endothermic reaction, that is the reverse reaction. ✓ The yield of ammonia would decrease. ✓

c) The temperature used in the Haber process is about 450 °C. Why not use a lower temperature and get a higher yield (see graph)?   [1 mark]

Student's answer   A lower temperature would give a higher yield but the reaction would be too slow to be economic. ✓

Examiner's comment   *The student has correctly discussed reaction rate and the economics of the process. The optimum temperature is about 450 °C, low enough to get a reasonable yield but high enough to have a rate of reaction that produces ammonia fast enough to be economical.*

> **Examiner's tip**
> Remember to learn:
>
> - 1:3 volume ratio N_2 : H_2
> - catalyst finely divided iron
> - pressure 200 atmospheres
> - optimum temperature about 450 °C.

Fertilisers

Plants need the three elements nitrogen, phosphorus and potassium for healthy growth. These are removed from the soil when plants are harvested. These essential plant nutrients are replaced by NPK fertilisers. A typical NPK fertiliser might contain ammonium nitrate, NH_4NO_3, ammonium phosphate, $(NH_4)_3PO_4$, and potassium chloride, KCl.

Ammonium salts are made using ammonia from the Haber process and an acid.

$$NH_3 + HNO_3 \rightarrow NH_4NO_3$$
$$2NH_3 + H_2SO_4 \rightarrow (NH_4)_2SO_4$$

Displacement of ammonia from its salts

This has been mentioned in Topic 12. The weak base, ammonia, is displaced from its salt by stronger bases.

$$(NH_4)_2SO_4 + Ca(OH)_2 \rightarrow CaSO_4 + 2NH_3 + 2H_2O$$

Formation of carbon dioxide

There are three methods by which carbon dioxide is formed:

- by the complete combustion of a carbon–based fuel
- in respiration, which occurs in the cells of plants and animals and provides energy for all living processes
- by the reaction of carbonates with acids to form a salt, carbon dioxide and water.

● **Try this**   *The answers are given on p. 125.*

5 **a)** Name three fossil fuels. [3 marks]
   b) Name two carbon-containing fuels that are not fossil fuels. [2 marks]
   c) Complete and balance this equation.

   $C_3H_8 + O_2 \rightarrow$ .... + ... [2 marks]

6 Balance this equation for a reaction, the oxidation of glucose, that is typical of respiration.

   $C_6H_{12}O_6 + O_2 \rightarrow CO_2 + H_2O$ [1 mark]

7 Complete the following equations for the reaction of acids and carbonates.

   zinc carbonate + nitric acid $\rightarrow$ .... + ... + ...

   $MgCO_3 + H_2SO_4 \rightarrow$ .... + ... + ...

   $NiCO_3 + 2H^+ \rightarrow$ .... + ... + ... [6 marks]

8 Natural gas is methane. It is used as a fuel.

   $CH_4 + 2O_2 \rightarrow CO_2 + 2H_2O$ complete combustion

   a) Write the equation for the incomplete combustion of methane. [2 marks]
   b) Explain why gas heaters should have a good supply of air and so should only be used in a well ventilated room. [2 marks]

9 **a)** Three common nitrogen-based fertilisers are:

ammonium sulphate	$(NH_4)_2SO_4$
ammonium nitrate	NH_4NO_3
urea	$CO(NH_2)_2$

   Calculate the percentage of nitrogen in each fertiliser. [6 marks]
   b) Two common phosphorus-based fertilisers are calcium superphosphate and ammonium phosphate.
   i) Calcium superphosphate is made from calcium phosphate which contains the ions Ca^{2+} and PO_4^{3-}. Write its formula. [1 mark]
   ii) What is the advantage of using ammonium phosphate compared with calcium superphosphate? [1 mark]
   iii) What is the third element essential for plant growth? [1 mark]

TOPIC 21 Sulphur

Key objectives

- To be able to name some sources of sulphur
- To know that the major use of sulphur is to provide sulphur dioxide for the Contact process
- To be able to name the uses of sulphur dioxide
- To be able to describe the manufacture of sulphuric acid by the Contact process
- To be able to describe the properties of sulphuric acid as a typical acid

Key ideas

Sources of sulphur

The element sulphur is found in underground sulphur beds in the USA, Mexico and Poland.

Natural gas and petroleum contain sulphur compounds. These have to be removed and are an important source of sulphur.

Metal sulphides occur as ores, for example zinc blende.

Uses of sulphur dioxide

The major use of sulphur dioxide is in the Contact process for the manufacture of sulphuric acid. It is also used as a bleach in the manufacture of paper from wood pulp, and as a preservative for food by killing bacteria.

Manufacture of sulphuric acid by the Contact process

Sulphur is burnt in air to form sulphur dioxide.

$$S + O_2 \rightarrow SO_2$$

This is mixed with oxygen to form sulphur trioxide.

$$2SO_2(g) + O_2(g) \rightleftharpoons 2SO_3(g) \quad \text{The forward reaction is exothermic.}$$

The reaction between sulphur trioxide and water is too violent to carry out directly. Sulphur trioxide is dissolved in concentrated sulphuric acid to give oleum. Water is added to form concentrated sulphuric acid.

$$SO_3 + H_2O \rightarrow H_2SO_4$$

Note that some textbooks give more complicated equations, as follows.

Dissolve sulphur trioxide in concentrated sulphuric acid to form oleum.

$$SO_3 + H_2SO_4 \rightarrow H_2S_2O_7$$

Add water to the oleum.

$$H_2S_2O_7 + H_2O \rightarrow 2H_2SO_4$$

If you can remember these, that is fine, otherwise learn the simpler equation above.

Examiner's tip

▶ Remember to learn the reaction conditions for the Contact process:

- catalyst vanadium(V) oxide
- optimum temperature 450 °C
- atmospheric pressure.

The reason for using an optimum temperature is that the forward reaction is exothermic, so there has to be a compromise between yield and rate. There is no need to use increased pressure even though there is a volume decrease. At atmospheric pressure the yield is 96%.

Sulphuric acid as a typical acid

See Topic 12.

● **Try this** *The answers are given on p. 125.*

1 Sulphuric acid is an important chemical both industrially and in the laboratory.

a) In the 18th century, sulphuric acid was manufactured by burning a mixture of sulphur and potassium nitrate. The mixture of gases formed was reacted with water. The sulphuric acid formed by this method was impure and expensive.

   i) The impure acid contained another acid. Suggest the name of this acid. [1 mark]

   ii) Write an equation for the action of heat on potassium nitrate. [2 marks]

b) In 1831, Philips, an English vinegar manufacturer, invented the Contact Process. It made pure concentrated sulphuric acid cheaply.

$$S + O_2 \rightarrow SO_2$$
$$2SO_2 + O_2 \rightleftharpoons 2SO_3$$
$$SO_3 + H_2O \rightarrow H_2SO_4$$

   i) Why is the Contact Process preferred to the older method of making sulphuric acid? [1 mark]

   ii) Sulphur dioxide is made by burning sulphur. Name a source of the element sulphur. [1 mark]

   iii) Name the catalyst used for the reaction between sulphur dioxide and oxygen. [1 mark]

   iv) What would be the effect of decreasing the temperature on the position of equilibrium in the reversible reaction between sulphur dioxide and oxygen? [2 marks]

   v) In the older process, sulphur trioxide was reacted directly with water. Describe how it is changed into sulphuric in the Contact Process. [2 marks]

   vi) State **two** large-scale uses of sulphuric acid. [2 marks]

c) Copper(II) sulphate-5-water was prepared by the following reactions.

$$CuO + H_2SO_4 \rightarrow CuSO_4 + H_2O$$
$$CuSO_4 + 5H_2O \rightarrow CuSO_4.5H_2O$$

In an experiment 25 cm³ of 2.0 mol/dm³ sulphuric acid was neutralised with an excess of copper(II) oxide. The yield of the crystals was 7.3 g. Complete the following to calculate the percentage yield.

   i) Number of moles of H_2SO_4 in 25 cm³ of 2.0 mol/dm³ = ...

   ii) Maximum number of moles of $CuSO_4.5H_2O$ that could be formed = ...

   iii) Maximum mass of $CuSO_4.5H_2O$ that could be formed = ...
Mass of one mole of $CuSO_4.5H_2O$ = 250 g

   iv) Percentage yield = ... [4 marks]

IGCSE Chemistry, May 1998, Q4

TOPIC 22 Carbonates

Key objectives

- To be able to describe the manufacture of calcium oxide from calcium carbonate
- To be able to describe the uses of lime and slaked lime
- To know that calcium carbonate is used in the manufacture of iron and of cement

Key ideas

Calcium compounds from calcium carbonate

Calcium carbonate is heated.

$$CaCO_3 \rightarrow CaO + CO_2$$
limestone   lime

Water is added to calcium oxide.

$$CaO + H_2O \rightarrow Ca(OH)_2$$
slaked lime

Note that an aqueous solution of calcium hydroxide is limewater. This goes milky in the presence of carbon dioxide.

$$Ca(OH)_2(aq) + CO_2(g) \rightarrow CaCO_3(s) + H_2O(l)$$

Uses of calcium compounds

Calcium oxide (lime) and calcium hydroxide (slaked lime) are both used to treat acidic soils and to neutralise acidic wastes.

Calcium carbonate has many uses:

- in the manufacture of cement
- in the manufacture of glass
- in the blast furnace and in steel making to remove silicon(IV) oxide as slag (see Topic 19) and
- to neutralise acidic soils and lakes caused by acid rain.

● Try this

The answers are given on p. 126.

1 A solid, **X**, reacts with water to form a different solid, **Y**. This dissolves in water. When carbon dioxide is bubbled through a solution of **Y**, a white precipitate, **Z**, forms. On heating precipitate **Z**, solid **X** and carbon dioxide are formed.

    a) Identify the three calcium compounds:

        solid **X**   solid **Y**   precipitate **Z**   [3 marks]

    b) Write equations for the three reactions.   [6 marks]

2 Calcium carbonate and calcium oxide are both bases. They are used in agriculture to reduce acidity in soil.

    a) Write an ionic equation for the reaction between calcium oxide and hydrogen ions.   [2 marks]

    b) Calcium oxide is a soluble base and calcium carbonate is an insoluble base.

       i) Predict the pH of the soil if an excess of calcium carbonate was used.   [1 mark]

       ii) Predict the pH of the soil if an excess of calcium oxide was used.   [1 mark]

TOPIC 23 Organic chemistry I

Key objectives

- To be able to name and draw the structures of methane, ethane, ethanol, ethanoic acid and the products of the reactions in the Core section of the syllabus
- To be able to name and draw the structures of the unbranched alkanes, alkenes, alcohols and acids containing up to four carbon atoms per molecule
- To be able to relate type of compound present to ending of the name
- To be able to name the fuels – coal, natural gas and petroleum
- To be able to describe the fractional distillation of petroleum and the uses of the various fractions
- To understand the concept of a homologous series
- To be able to describe the general characteristics of a homologous series
- To be able to describe and recognise structural isomerism
- To be able to describe the properties of the alkanes with particular reference to methane
- To be able to describe substitution reactions of alkanes with chlorine
- To be able to describe the bonding in alkanes
- To understand that cracking can be used to manufacture alkenes, hydrogen and more useful hydrocarbons
- To be able to describe the addition reactions of alkenes with hydrogen, bromine and steam
- To be able to distinguish between saturated and unsaturated hydrocarbons from their structures and by a simple chemical test
- To be able to describe the formation of poly(ethene) by addition polymerisation
- To be able to describe the formation of ethanol by fermentation and by an addition reaction
- To be able to describe the burning of ethanol and to name its uses as a solvent and a fuel
- To be able to describe the formation of ethanoic acid by the oxidation of ethanol
- To know that ethanoic acid is a typical weak acid
- To be able to describe the formation of an ester from ethanoic acid and ethanol

Key ideas   Fuels

- Coal has been formed by the anaerobic decay of vegetation over millions of years. Anaerobic means in the absence of oxygen.
- Natural gas is mainly methane (CH_4).
- Petroleum, or crude oil, is a complex mixture of hydrocarbons.

Fractional distillation of petroleum

Fractional distillation separates petroleum into more useful mixtures of hydrocarbons, called fractions. The process works because the fractions have different boiling point ranges. See Figure 23.1.

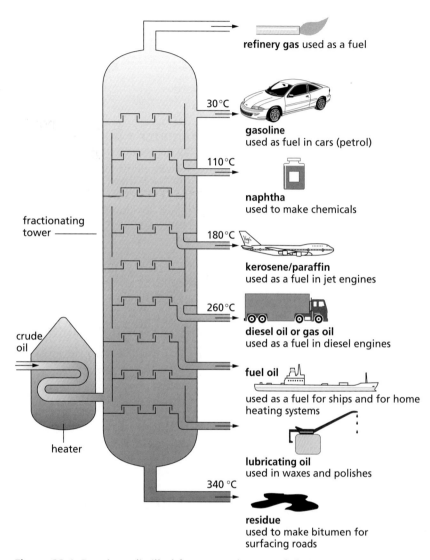

Figure 23.1 Fractions distilled from petroleum and their uses

Homologous series

The hydrocarbons in petroleum belong to a family or *homologous series* called the alkanes. The names of all members of this series end in '–ane'.

The characteristics of a homologous series are as follows.

- All members of the series can be represented by a general formula. For example, for the alkanes, this is C_nH_{2n+2}, where n is the number of carbon atoms in the molecule.
- Consecutive members of the series differ by CH_2.
- They have similar chemical properties because they have the same functional group. For example, all alkenes have $C=C$, all organic acids have $-COOH$, etc.
- Their physical properties change in a predictable way, for example the boiling points of the alkanes increase as n increases.

Properties of the alkanes

Alkane	Formula	Boiling point/°C	Physical state at r.t.p.
Methane	CH_4	−162	Gas
Ethane	C_2H_6	−89	Gas
Propane	C_3H_8	−42	Gas
Butane	C_4H_{10}	0	Gas
Pentane	C_5H_{12}	36	Liquid
Hexane	C_6H_{14}	69	Liquid

Examiner's tips
▶ All names end in '-ane', all formulae follow the pattern C_nH_{2n+2}, and the boiling points increase as the molecules get bigger. Note the pattern.
▶ Although there is a general increase, the difference in boiling points between consecutive members is getting smaller. It is possible to predict boiling points of higher members – the boiling point of heptane (C_7H_{16}) is predicted to be 96 to 99 °C. Can you see why?

Alkanes have only single bonds. No more atoms can add on to the molecule so they are described as *saturated hydrocarbons*. They are generally unreactive except for combustion and chlorination.

Combustion of alkanes

The complete combustion of an alkane gives carbon dioxide and water.

$$CH_4 + 2O_2 \rightarrow CO_2 + 2H_2O$$

$$2C_2H_6 + 7O_2 \rightarrow 4CO_2 + 6H_2O$$

The incomplete combustion of an alkane gives carbon monoxide and water.

Substitution reactions of alkanes

Alkanes react with chlorine in bright light to give a mixture of chloroalkanes. One hydrogen atom is substituted by one chlorine atom.

$$CH_4 + Cl_2 \rightarrow CH_3Cl + HCl$$
chloromethane

Provided there is enough chlorine present, the reaction can continue until all four hydrogen atoms have been substituted.

$$CH_3Cl + Cl_2 \rightarrow CH_2Cl_2 + HCl$$
dichloromethane

$$CH_2Cl_2 + Cl_2 \rightarrow CHCl_3 + HCl$$
trichloromethane

$$CHCl_3 + Cl_2 \rightarrow CCl_4 + HCl$$
tetrachloromethane

The number of hydrogen and chlorine atoms must add up to four.

The reaction is photochemical: alkanes and chlorine do not react in the dark.

Other alkanes also give substitution reactions with chlorine.

$$C_3H_8 + Cl_2 \rightarrow C_3H_7Cl + HCl$$

propane   chloropropane

Structures of the alkanes

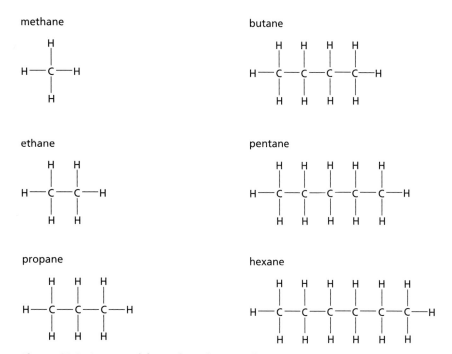

Figure 23.2 Structural formulae of some alkanes

In these structural formulae, Figure 23.2, every covalent bond is represented by a single line. Each covalent bond is a shared pair of electrons, one electron from each atom.

Structures can also be represented using the following notation.

$$CH_3{-}CH_2{-}CH_2{-}CH_3$$

This is the formula for butane.

Common error

It is very easy to make a mistake using this type of formula. The number of bonds per carbon atom, that is lines and hydrogen atoms, must equal four. Always check carefully and avoid common errors of the type shown below. What is wrong with these formulae?

$$CH_3{-}CH{-}CH_3 \quad \text{and} \quad CH_3{-}CH_2(CH_3){-}CH_2{-}CH_3$$

In the first formula the central carbon has a valency of 3 not 4. The formula ought to be $CH_3{-}CH_2{-}CH_3$. The second carbon in the other formula has a valency of 5. The correct formula is $CH_3{-}CH(CH_3){-}CH_2{-}CH_3$. ■

Isomerism

Isomers are different compounds that have the same molecular formula but different structural formulae.

> **Examiner's tip**
> ▶ The above definition of isomers is very important. It would be a good idea to learn it by heart.

Common error

Typical mistakes are to state that isomers are different forms of the same compound, to confuse isomers and isotopes, and to leave out the key words – molecular and structural. ■

An example of isomerism is given by the two compounds with molecular formula C_4H_{10} – see Figure 23.3.

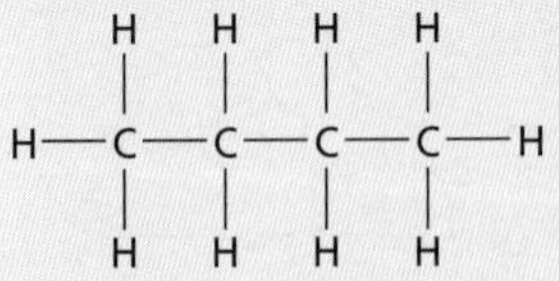

Names of alkanes

You do not need to learn how to name branched alkanes but it is helpful to be aware of how organic chemicals are named. Look at 2-methylpropane in Figure 23.3.

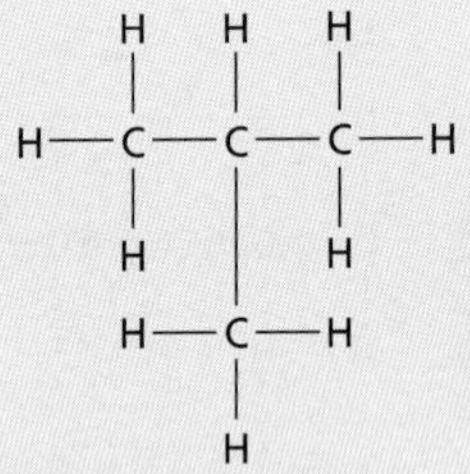

- Look for the longest chain, here three carbon atoms, so part of the name is propane (the third alkane).
- Look for side groups, here CH_3 which has one carbon atom, so it is called methyl.
- Look at the position of this group: count along the chain, it is on the second carbon. The name is therefore 2-methylpropane. (In this example the '2' is redundant, as there is only one position possible for the methyl and that is on the central carbon atom, but it illustrates the principle.)

H—C—C—C—C—H melting point –138°C

butane boiling point 0°C

H—C—C—C—H melting point –159°C

H—C—H boiling point –12°C

2-methylpropane

Figure 23.3 The isomers of C_4H_{10}

Sample questions and answers

Sample question 1 What is the molecular formula of the C_{12} alkane? [1 mark]

Student's answer $C_{12}H_{26}$ ✓

Examiner's comment *Correct. Double the number of carbon atoms and add 2 to find the number of hydrogen atoms.*

Sample question 2 Which of the following are hydrocarbons and which are alkanes?

$C_{10}H_{20}$ C_7H_{16} $C_4H_{10}O$ $C_{22}H_{44}$ [2 marks]

Student's answer They are all hydrocarbons. ✗ C_7H_{16} is the only alkane. ✓

Examiner's comment *$C_4H_{10}O$ is not a hydrocarbon since hydrocarbons contain carbon and hydrogen only. Yes, C_7H_{16} is the only alkane, it corresponds to the general formula C_nH_{2n+2}.*

Sample question 3   Draw the structural formulae of two isomers of C_5H_{12}.

[2 marks]

Student's answer

CH_3—CH_2—CH_2—CH_2—CH_3 ✓

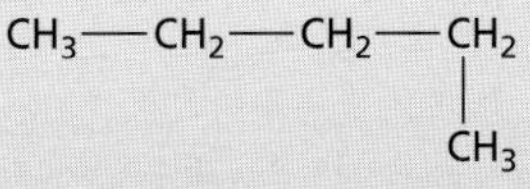

CH_3—CH_2—CH_2—CH_2
                                    | ✗
                                  CH_3

Examiner's comment   *No, these are the same molecule – they both have five carbon atoms in a chain.*

Model answer   Any two from the following structural formulae:

CH_3—CH_2—CH_2—CH_2—CH_3

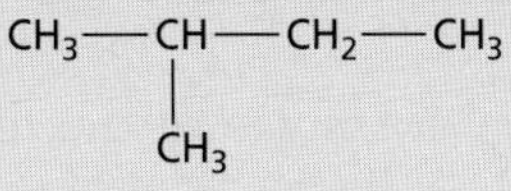

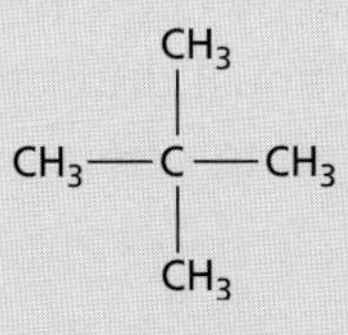

CH_3—CH—CH_2—CH_3
              |
            CH_3

          CH_3
            |
CH_3—C—CH_3
            |
          CH_3

Sample question 4   One mole of butane reacted with one mole of chlorine to give two different products with the molecular formulae C_4H_9Cl. Give the structural formulae of these products.   [2 marks]

Student's answer   Two isomers have been formed:

CH_3—CH_2—CH_2—CH_2—Cl ✓

Cl—CH_2—CH_2—CH_2—CH_3 ✗

Examiner's comment   *No, these two structures are the same – the second one is a 180° rotation of the first one.*

Model answer   The isomers are as shown here:

CH_3—CH_2—CH_2—CH_2—Cl

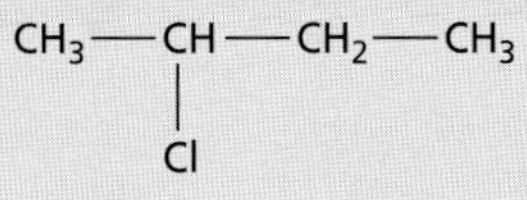

CH_3—CH—CH_2—CH_3
              |
            Cl

Alkenes

Alkenes are a homologous series of *unsaturated* hydrocarbons. Their general formula is C_nH_{2n}. They all have a double bond and can undergo addition reactions. Their names all end in '-ene'. The first alkene is ethene. Figure 23.4 shows the arrangement of the valency electrons in a molecule of ethene.

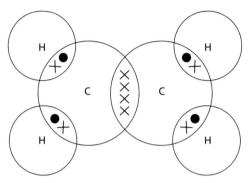

Figure 23.4 The bonding in ethene, the simplest alkene

ethene

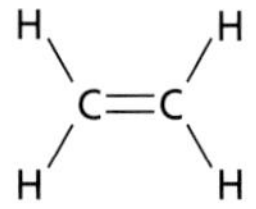

propene

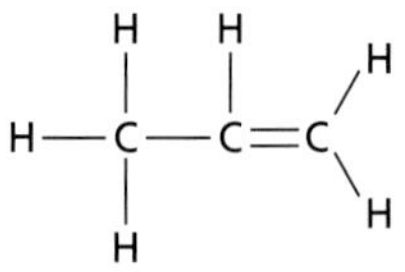

butene

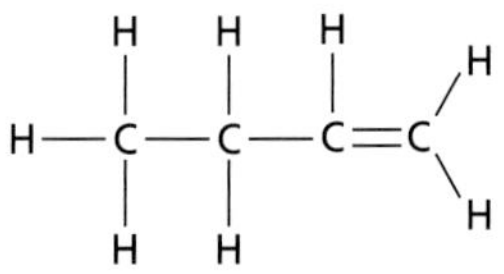

Figure 23.5 Structural formulae of some alkenes

The structural formulae of the first three alkenes are given in Figure 23.5.

Alkenes are made by cracking alkanes. Large alkane molecules, obtained by the fractional distillation of petroleum, are passed over a heated catalyst consisting of silicon(IV) oxide and aluminium oxide.

$$C_{10}H_{22}(g) \quad \rightarrow \quad C_8H_{18}(g) \quad + \quad C_2H_4(g)$$
higher alkane simpler alkane alkene
decane   octane   ethene

There are many different products that can be obtained by the cracking of decane. Another possibility is shown in the next equation.

$$C_{10}H_{22}(g) \quad \rightarrow \quad C_7H_{16}(g) \quad + \quad C_3H_6(g)$$
higher alkane simpler alkane alkene

Hydrogen can also be made by cracking.

$$C_{10}H_{22}(g) \quad \rightarrow \quad C_7H_{14}(g) \quad + \quad C_3H_6(g) \quad + \quad H_2(g)$$
higher alkane   alkene   alkene

This type of cracking gives a mixture of alkenes and hydrogen. Cracking is used to make:

- alkenes
- hydrogen
- petrol from the higher fractions, since there is a greater demand for petrol than for kerosene.

Addition reactions

In an addition reaction two reactants form a single product. Hydrogen reacts with an alkene to form an alkane. This type of reaction is called hydrogenation and is used to make margarine from unsaturated vegetable oils.

$$C_2H_4 + H_2 \quad \rightarrow \quad C_2H_6$$
$$180\,^{\circ}C$$
nickel catalyst

Water reacts with an alkene to give an alcohol. This type of reaction is called hydration.

$$C_2H_4(g) + H_2O(g) \quad \rightarrow \quad C_2H_5OH(g)$$
steam $\quad$ 300 $^{\circ}$C $\quad$ ethanol
phosphoric acid
catalyst
60 atmospheres

Test for an alkene

Bromine dissolved in water can be used to distinguish between unsaturated hydrocarbons, alkenes, and saturated hydrocarbons, alkanes. When a few drops of bromine water are added to a tube of ethene gas, the colour changes from brown or orange to colourless.

$$C_2H_4(g) + Br_2(aq) \rightarrow C_2H_4Br_2 \quad \text{This is dibromoethane.}$$
brown $\quad$ colourless

This reaction occurs with an alkene because the bromine molecule can add across the double bond. Bromine water does not react with alkanes because there is no double bond.

Examiner's tip
▶ If you are asked to describe this test you should state that the bromine water goes from brown to colourless with the alkene, and that the bromine water remains brown with the alkane. Remember to say colourless not clear – bromine water is clear but it is not colourless.

$$nC_2H_4 \longrightarrow \left(CH_2 - CH_2 \right)_n$$

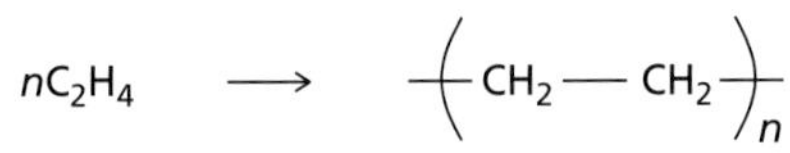

Figure 23.6 Addition polymerisation

Addition polymerisation

Polymerisation is the formation of long chain molecules called polymers from a large number of monomer molecules.

Figure 23.6 shows addition polymerisation because there is only one product, the polymer.

> **Examiner's tip**
> ▶ When you are drawing the structure of a polymer, check that the repeat unit is correct and that your diagram indicates a long chain and continuation.

There is a more detailed discussion of polymers in Topic 24.

Alcohols

> **Examiner's tip**
> ▶ Remember, for the Core you only need to study ethanol.

All alcohols have −OH as the functional group. The general formula is $C_nH_{2n+1}OH$. Their names all end in '-ol'. With propanol and butanol, the number in the name gives the position of the −OH group on the chain. See Figure 23.7 opposite.

Ethanol can be manufactured

- from ethene (see the hydration of ethene, p. 101)
- by fermentation (see Topic 25).

Ethanol burns with a clean flame. It is used in camping stoves and, in some countries, is used alone or mixed with petrol as a fuel for cars.

$$C_2H_5OH + 3O_2 \rightarrow 2CO_2 + 3H_2O$$
combustion

> **Examiner's tip**
> ▶ Take care with balancing this equation. It is easy to forget that ethanol contains oxygen and that there are six hydrogen atoms in total.

Ethanol is used

- as a fuel (see above)
- as a solvent in the perfume and food industries
- in some cultures in alcoholic drinks
- to make other organic chemicals such as esters.

methanol	CH_3OH	

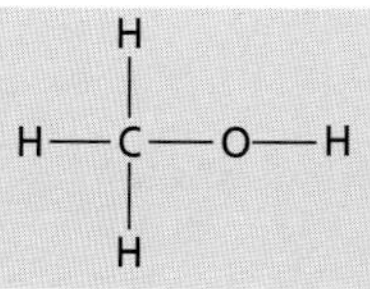

$$\begin{array}{c} H \\ | \\ H-C-O-H \\ | \\ H \end{array}$$

ethanol	CH_3CH_2OH	

$$\begin{array}{c} H \quad H \\ | \quad | \\ H-C-C-O-H \\ | \quad | \\ H \quad H \end{array}$$

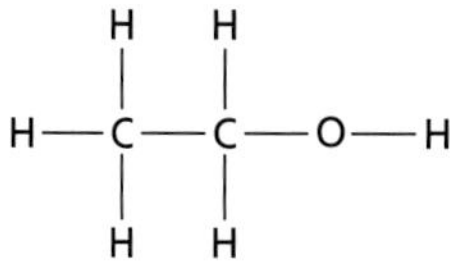

propanol or propan-1-ol	$CH_3CH_2CH_2OH$	

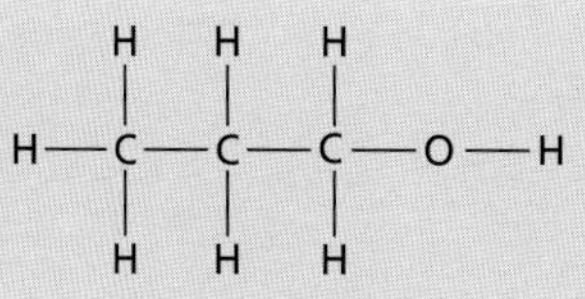

$$\begin{array}{c} H \quad H \quad H \\ | \quad | \quad | \\ H-C-C-C-O-H \\ | \quad | \quad | \\ H \quad H \quad H \end{array}$$

propan 2-ol	$CH_3CH(OH)CH_3$	

$$\begin{array}{c} H \quad H \quad H \\ | \quad | \quad | \\ H-C-C-C-H \\ | \quad | \quad | \\ H \quad O \quad H \\ | \\ H \end{array}$$

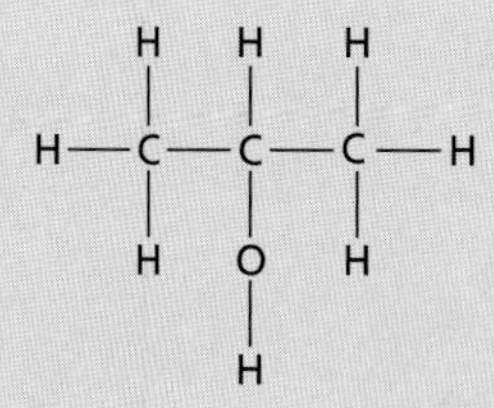

butanol or butan-1-ol	$CH_3CH_2CH_2CH_2OH$	

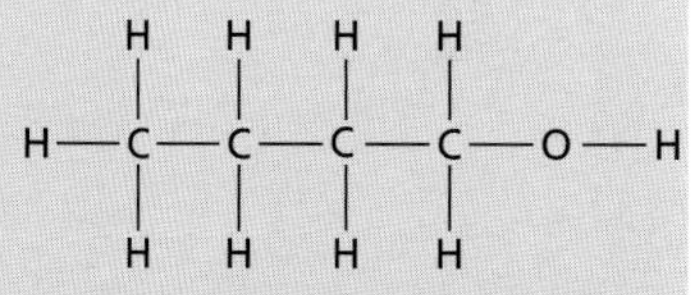

$$\begin{array}{c} H \quad H \quad H \quad H \\ | \quad | \quad | \quad | \\ H-C-C-C-C-O-H \\ | \quad | \quad | \quad | \\ H \quad H \quad H \quad H \end{array}$$

butan-2-ol	$CH_3CH(OH)CH_2CH_3$	

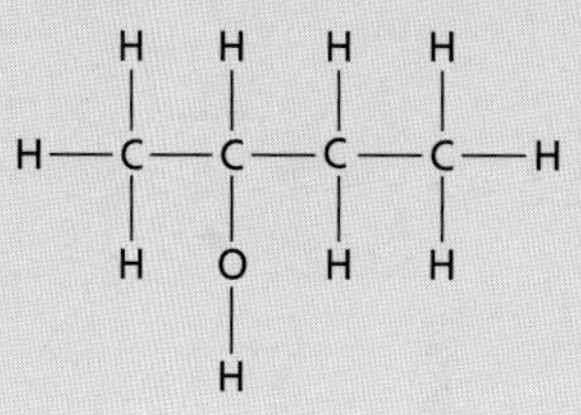

$$\begin{array}{c} H \quad H \quad H \quad H \\ | \quad | \quad | \quad | \\ H-C-C-C-C-H \\ | \quad | \quad | \quad | \\ H \quad O \quad H \quad H \\ | \\ H \end{array}$$

Figure 23.7 The alcohols

Organic acids

All organic acids have the functional group $-COOH$ or $-CO_2H$. The general formula is $C_nH_{2n+1}COOH$ and all their names end in '-oic acid':

methanoic acid $HCOOH$ – the acid in nettle stings

ethanoic acid CH_3COOH – the acid in vinegar

propanoic acid CH_3CH_2COOH

butanoic acid $CH_3CH_2CH_2COOH$

Remember you must count the carbon atoms in the acid group. Butanoic acid has a total of four carbon atoms.

Some alcohols oxidise to organic acids. Ethanol is oxidised to ethanoic acid. This is why when wine is left exposed to the air it smells of vinegar.

$$CH_3CH_2OH + O_2 \rightarrow CH_3COOH + H_2O$$
$$\text{from the air}$$

When ethanol is heated with the oxidising agent acidified potassium dichromate(VI), ethanoic acid is formed.

$$CH_3CH_2OH + 2O \rightarrow CH_3COOH + H_2O$$

from the
oxidising
agent

The full equation is complicated.

All organic acids are weak acids. In aqueous solution they are only partially ionised. They have all the typical acid properties – see Topic 12.

To name the salts of organic acids, remove the '–ic acid' and add '–ate'.

metal + acid $\rightarrow$ salt + hydrogen

$$Mg(s) + 2CH_3COOH(aq) \rightarrow (CH_3COO)_2Mg(aq) + H_2(g)$$

magnesium ethanoate

base + acid $\rightarrow$ salt + water

$$NaOH(aq) + CH_3COOH(aq) \rightarrow CH_3COONa(aq) + H_2O(l)$$

$$MgO(s) + 2CH_3COOH(aq) \rightarrow (CH_3COO)_2Mg(aq) + H_2O(l)$$

carbonate + acid $\rightarrow$ salt + carbon dioxide + water

$$Na_2CO_3(aq) + 2CH_3COOH(aq) \rightarrow$$
$$2CH_3COONa(aq) + CO_2(g) + H_2O(l)$$

Esters

Organic acids react with alcohols to form an ester and water.

$$CH_3COOH + CH_3CH_2OH \rightarrow CH_3COOCH_2CH_3 + H_2O$$

heat
concentrated
sulphuric acid
catalyst

The ester is ethyl ethanoate and it has the structure shown in Figure 23.8.

Esters have a 'fruity' smell and are used as food flavourings.

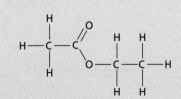

Figure 23.8 Structural formula of ethyl ethanoate

Examiner's tips

▶ Be careful with the formula for ethyl ethanoate – for example $CH_3COOCH_3CH_2$ is wrong, it should be $CH_3COOCH_2CH_3$.
▶ $CH_3CH_2COOCH_3$ is not ethyl ethanoate, it is methyl propanoate. Remember when writing the name of an ester that the group from the alcohol, e.g. methyl, comes before the part from the acid, e.g. propanoate.

● **Try this**   *The answers are given on p. 126.*

Remember that if two organic compounds have the same functional group, then they will have the same chemical properties. Many of the following questions involve predicting the properties of less familiar compounds using this idea.

Note that some question parts involve topics from the syllabus Supplement.

1   For each of the following formulae, state the type of organic compound.

[6 marks]

   A $CH_3–CH(OH)–CH_3$
   B $C_{12}H_{24}$
   C $CH_3–CH_2–CH_2–CH_2–COOH$
   D $CH_3–(CH_2)_{10}–CH_3$
   E $C_2H_5COOC_3H_7$
   F $CH_3–CH_2–CH_2–CH_2–CH_2–Cl$

2   Complete the following word equations.
   i)   methanoic acid + zinc →
   ii)   propanoic acid + copper(II) oxide →
   iii) butanoic acid + sodium carbonate →
   iv)   butene + bromine →
   v)   ethanoic acid + butanol →
   vi)   pentene + hydrogen →
   vii) propene + water →
   viii) ethane + chlorine →
   ix)   propanol + oxygen (excess) →
   x)   methanoic acid + propanol →   [20 marks]

3   Write symbol equations for the following reactions.
   i)   propanoic acid and sodium hydroxide
   ii) methanoic acid and magnesium
   iii) butanoic acid and sodium carbonate
   iv) the incomplete combustion of methane
   v)   ethanoic acid and methanol
   vi) propene and bromine   [12 marks]

4   Copy and complete the equations for the following cracking reactions.
   i) $C_8H_{18} \rightarrow C_4H_{10} + 2......$
   ii) $C_7H_{16} \rightarrow C_5H_{12} + ...$
   iii) $C_9H_{20} \rightarrow C_6H_{12} + C_3H_6 + ...$ [6 marks]

TOPIC 24 Organic chemistry II: synthetic macromolecules

Key objectives

- To be able to explain the term macromolecule
- To know that polymerisation is the formation of polymers from monomers
- To be able to deduce the structure of the polymer from that of the monomer
- To be able to deduce the structure of the monomer from that of the polymer
- To know the difference between addition polymerisation and condensation polymerisation
- To be able to describe the formation of a polyamide, nylon, and a polyester, terylene
- To know some of the uses of plastics and synthetic fibres
- To describe the pollution problems caused by non-biodegradable plastics

Key definitions

Macromolecule	A very large molecule made of repeating units. These units can be atoms as in diamond, simple molecules of ethene in poly(ethene), or more complex molecules as in proteins and polyamides
Monomer	Small molecules that join together to form one large polymer molecule
Polymer	A very large molecule formed from many monomer molecules
Addition polymerisation	The formation of one product, that is the polymer
Condensation polymerisation	A reaction in which there are two products, the polymer and a small molecule, e.g. water
Non-biodegradable	Not broken down in the environment by micro-organisms in the presence of water and oxygen

Key ideas

Addition polymerisation

Alkenes can take part in addition reactions. The carbon–carbon double bond changes to a single bond and alkene molecules can form a long chain – a polymer.

Poly(chloroethene), for example, known as PVC, is formed from the monomer chloroethene. See Figure 24.1.

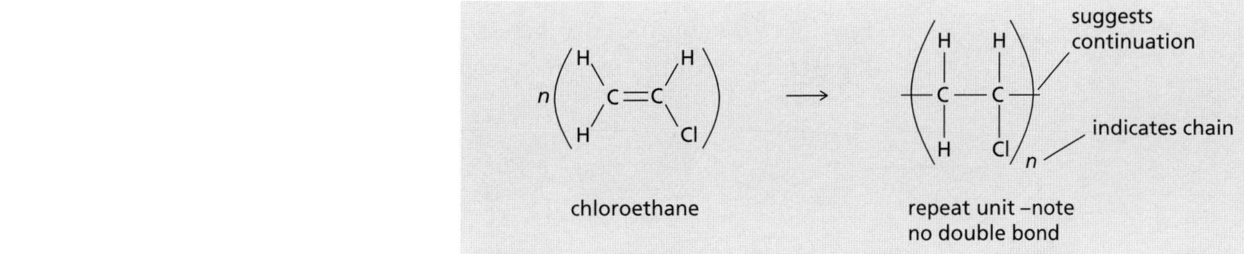

Figure 24.1 The monomer and the repeat unit of PVC

To deduce the structure of the monomer from that of the polymer, draw the structure of the repeat unit in the polymer then draw a double bond between the two carbon atoms that were in the chain. The name of the monomer is that of the polymer without the 'poly-' and brackets. Another example is shown in Figure 24.2.

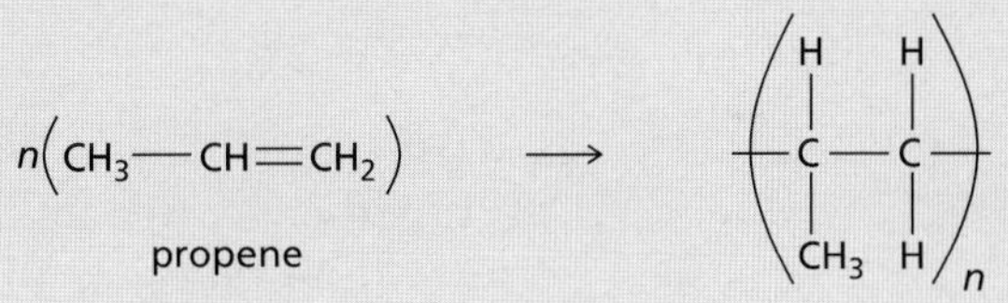

Figure 24.2 The monomer and the repeat unit of poly(propene)

Condensation polymerisation

In a condensation reaction, usually two monomers react together and join. During the reaction a molecule of water is often lost (see Figure 24.4 below).

In polyamides, the two monomers are as shown in Figure 24.3.

Figure 24.3 The two monomers that form a polyamide

They are joined together by an amide linkage, Figure 24.4, hence the name polyamide.

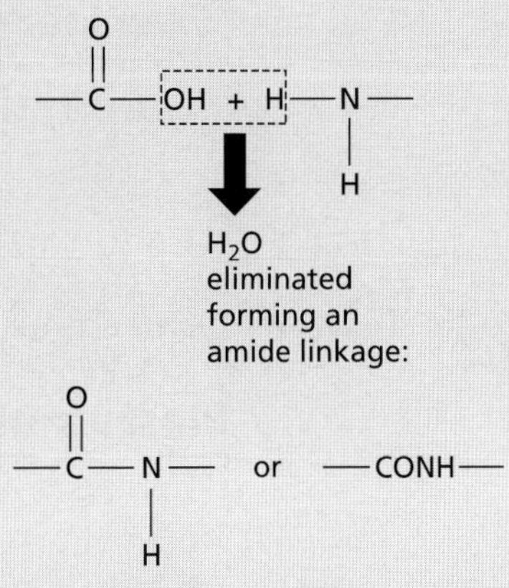

Figure 24.4 The formation of an amide linkage in condensation polymerisation

The reaction continues to give a long chain. Nylon is a polyamide. The structure of nylon can be represented as in Figure 24.5.

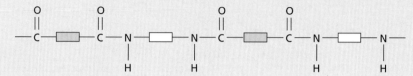

Figure 24.5 The structure of nylon

In polyesters, the two monomers are as shown in Figure 24.6.

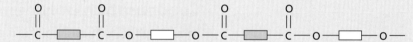

Figure 24.6 The two monomers that form a polyester

An ester linkage is formed and, as the polymer molecule is held together by this linkage, it is called a polyester. The reaction continues to give a long chain. The structure of a polyester can be represented as in Figure 24.7.

Figure 24.7 The structure of a polyester

A typical polyester is terylene.

Uses of polymers

- Nylon and terylene are used to make clothes.
- Nylon is used for rope making.
- PVC is used as an electrical insulator, for pipes and guttering.
- Poly(ethene) is used to make bowls, buckets, plastic bags, and as an electrical insulator.

Examiner's tip
▶ You do not need detailed knowledge, just a general awareness of the uses of polymers.

Sample question 1 Give two uses of polymers. [2 marks]

Model answer Garden furniture ✓ and window frames. ✓

Plastics and pollution

Polymers are non-biodegradable, that is, they do not decay. They are a major source of visual pollution and fill up available waste sites. Burning them is not a satisfactory solution to their disposal, since poisonous gases are formed. The best long-term solution to disposal would be to recycle polymer waste.

Common error

Do not write that these gases are 'harmful'. They should be described as 'toxic' or 'poisonous'. A common mistake is to think that sulphur dioxide would be formed and contribute to acid rain. The majority of plastics do not contain sulphur. Another misconception is that the emission of carbon monoxide would be a particular problem. This is formed by the incomplete combustion of *any* carbon-containing substance: coal, natural gas, liquid fuels, wood or plastics. This very poisonous gas presents a general problem and not one peculiar to plastics. ■

Examiner's tip

▶ It is sufficient to state that the gases are poisonous. If you name specific gases, they must be correct; for example, hydrogen chloride and hydrogen cyanide.

● **Try this** *The answers are given on p. 126.*

1 Deduce the structure of the monomers from the structure of the polymers shown in Figure 24.8. [2 marks]

i)

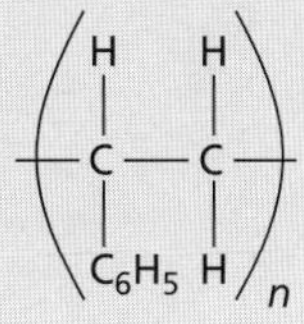

ii)

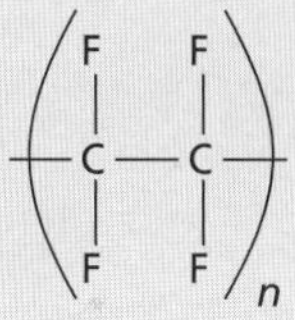

Figure 24.8

2 Deduce the structure of the polymers from those of the monomers shown in Figure 24.9. [2 marks]

i)

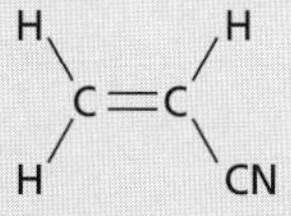

ii)

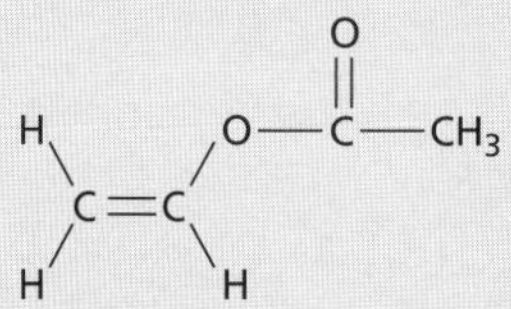

Figure 24.9

3 Give the structure of the polyamide that could be made from the two monomers

$$H_2N(CH_2)_6NH_2 \quad \text{and} \quad HOOC(CH_2)_4COOH$$ [2 marks]

4 Nylon is a synthetic macromolecule which is held together by the same linkage as protein molecules.
   a) What is the name of this linkage? [1 mark]
   b) Draw a diagram of the structure of nylon. [3 marks]
   c) Name another synthetic macromolecule which, like nylon, is made by condensation polymerisation. [1 mark]

TOPIC 25 Organic chemistry III: natural macromolecules

Key objectives
- To be able to name the three main constituents of food
- To know that proteins have the same amide linkage as nylon but with different repeat units
- To be able to describe the hydrolysis of proteins to amino acids
- To know that these amino acids can be identified by chromatography
- To know that fats are esters with the same linkage as terylene
- To know that the alkaline hydrolysis of fats produces soaps
- To be able to describe complex carbohydrates as condensation polymers of simple sugars
- To know that the acid hydrolysis of a complex carbohydrate gives simple sugars
- To be aware that these simple sugars can be identified by chromatography
- To be able to describe the fermentation of simple sugars to produce ethanol and carbon dioxide

Key ideas

The three main constituents of food are proteins, fats and carbohydrates.

Proteins

Proteins have the same amide linkage as nylon (see p. 108). The monomers are amino acids. Proteins can be hydrolysed back to amino acids by heating with hydrochloric acid. The amino acids formed can be identified by chromatography (see Topic 2).

$$\text{amino acids} \quad \rightarrow \quad \text{protein + water}$$
$$\text{condensation}$$
$$\text{polymerisation}$$

$$\text{protein + water} \quad \rightarrow \quad \text{amino acids}$$
$$\text{hydrolysis}$$
$$\text{(boil with}$$
$$\text{hydrochloric acid)}$$

There can be up to 20 different amino acids in a protein.

Fats

Both animal fats and vegetable oils are esters. A typical fat is glyceryl stearate, Figure 25.1.

Fats can be hydrolysed by heating with aqueous sodium hydroxide.

$$C_{17}H_{35}COOCH_2$$
$$|$$
$$C_{17}H_{35}COOCH$$
$$|$$
$$C_{17}H_{35}COOCH_2$$

Figure 25.1 Structural formula of a typical fat, glyceryl stearate

$$\text{fat} + \frac{\text{sodium}}{\text{hydroxide}} \rightarrow \frac{\text{sodium salt of}}{\text{a long-chain}} + \text{glycerol}$$
$$\text{organic acid}$$

For example:

glyceryl stearate + sodium hydroxide → sodium stearate + glycerol (Figure 25.2)

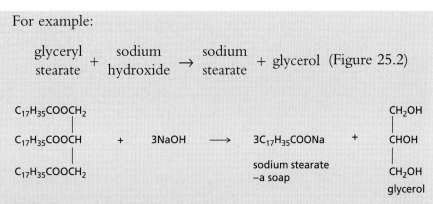

Figure 25.2 Hydrolysis of glyceryl stearate

> **Examiner's tip**
> ► You do not need to learn the structure or the full equation for the hydrolysis of a fat but they may be given in a question. You do need to know the word equation.

Sample question 1
a) What class of compound is olive oil? [1 mark]
b) What class of compound is glycerol? [1 mark]
c) What does the word hydrolysis mean? [1 mark]
d) What is the main use of compounds such as sodium stearate? [1 mark]

Student's answer
a) It is an ester. ✓
b) Glycerol is an alcohol. ✓
c) Hydrolysis is a type of chemical reaction in which a compound reacts with water to form two or more compounds. ✓
d) They are soaps. ✓

Examiner's comment *All answers are correct.*

Carbohydrates

Carbohydrates contain only the elements carbon, hydrogen and oxygen. The ratio of hydrogen to oxygen atoms is 2:1 (as in water, hence 'hydrate'). Glucose and starch are both carbohydrates. Glucose, $C_6H_{12}O_6$, is a simple sugar, and starch, $(C_6H_{10}O_5)_n$, is a complex carbohydrate. Glucose can be represented as in Figure 25.3. Starch can be represented as in Figure 25.4.

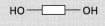

Figure 25.3 Structure of glucose

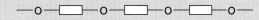

Figure 25.4 Structure of starch

glucose → starch + water

This is condensation polymerisation (see Topic 24, p. 107) – a polymer or macromolecule forms and water is eliminated.

Acid hydrolysis of complex carbohydrates

When complex carbohydrates are heated with dilute hydrochloric acid, they are hydrolysed to sugars.

starch + water → glucose

The acid is a catalyst for this reaction. The reaction can also be catalysed by enzymes, but the sugar produced is not necessarily the same as when acid catalyst is used.

Sugars formed by the hydrolysis of complex carbohydrates can be identified using chromatography.

Fermentation

Fermentation forms ethanol and carbon dioxide from glucose.

glucose → ethanol + carbon dioxide

This reaction is catalysed by the enzymes from yeast.

Sample question 2

a) Explain why fermentation must be carried out in the absence of air. [2 marks]

b) The best temperature for fermentation is about 35 °C. What are the disadvantages of using a lower or a much higher temperature? [2 marks]

c) When the concentration of ethanol reaches about 14%, fermentation ceases. Suggest a reason. [1 mark]

d) Complete the equation for fermentation:

$$C_6H_{12}O_6 \rightarrow$$ [2 marks]

Model answers

a) Because the oxygen in the air would oxidise ✓ the ethanol to carbon dioxide ✓ *or* fermentation is the anaerobic respiration ✓✓ of yeast cells.

b) At a lower temperature the rate would be slower ✓ and at a higher temperature the enzymes would be denatured (destroyed).✓

c) Ethanol is poisonous to yeast, and at this concentration yeast dies ✓ *or* all the glucose has been used up.✓

d) $C_6H_{12}O_6 \rightarrow 2C_2H_5OH$✓ $+ 2CO_2$✓

Examiner's tip

▶ You do not need to learn the formula for glucose. If it is required to answer the question, it will be given.

Preparing for the examination

During the course

Preparing for an external examination is a continuous process throughout the course. All the activities, lessons, homework, practical work and assessments are major factors in determining the final examination grade, so the first piece of advice is to suggest that you work steadily throughout the two years of the course. It is essential that you prepare thoroughly for internal school examinations, then, as you approach the IGCSE examination and start your revision programme, the topics will be familiar and the learning process will be less stressful and more productive.

Make sure that your notes are up to date. If you miss work through absence, either copy it from a friend or leave a comment in your notes that will remind you to refer to the topic in a textbook. Similarly, look at any homework you have missed and if it involves the reinforcement of skills or concepts, then it would be a good idea to photocopy it. This may not be a popular suggestion but you must realise that not all homework assignments are of equal value – some are integral components of the course. You will need to make a judgement, but to help you here is some general advice: problems, equation writing, factual material that is not covered elsewhere in your scheme of work and past questions should be photocopied or, even better, you should complete the assignments on your return.

In summary:

- work steadily throughout the course
- ensure that your work is both complete and accurate
- make sure that you understand the ideas and concepts
- if you find an aspect of the course difficult seek assistance
- learn the topics for tests and internal examinations.

Revision techniques

Well in advance of the examination, produce a revision timetable for all your subjects, but be realistic and include time for relaxation and socialising. Then create a more detailed one for chemistry, to cover all the topics. Ideally you ought to go through the complete course twice. Keep a checklist of the topics studied – it is encouraging to have a visual record of your progress.

It is useful to have a copy of the syllabus but not essential, as this book includes all the information required for IGCSE Chemistry. You will need a quiet room at a comfortable temperature, plenty of paper and a pencil or pen. Some students find doodling (chemistry of course) with coloured pens helpful. On occasion, revising with a friend makes a welcome and useful change. You will have to discover for how long you can profitably study – this is a very individual characteristic and can vary from person to person, maybe as little as 30 minutes or over an hour. Do not exceed your revision time, and break up the available time into study sessions and breaks. You might want to introduce rewards – 'When I have finished this section of work I will ....'.

Revision must be active – do not believe that just looking at a book is an effective way of learning. You could make flash cards that have bullet lists of essential points. You could study the topic for several minutes and then close the book and write out what you can remember (without taking great care over presentation), then check your account against the book. Repeat this until you have most of the information correct, then move on to another section of the work. This is the 'look, cover, write and check' technique, and it is very effective for the majority of students. It is crucial that you repeat this technique on the same topic, at least once but preferably twice, in the fairly near future, that is, either later the same day or the next day. This will greatly increase the long-term retention of the topic.

Keeping a list of important words is useful. You could write the words on one side of a card and the meanings on the other. Then when you have an odd few minutes you can brush up on your chemistry vocabulary.

Once you have acquired a reasonably good knowledge and understanding of the course, it is time to extend your revision to practising on past papers. This is a most valuable form of preparation; not only does it provide a test of the effectiveness of your revision but it provides an insight of what to expect in the 'real' examination.

The examination syllabus gives a full list of the terms used by examiners and how candidates are expected to respond. Commonly used terms are:

- 'Define' – you need to give a precise statement
- 'What do you understand by?' – give the definition and some additional explanation
- 'State' – give a concise answer, no explanation is needed
- 'Explain' – you must give reasons and/or underlying theory
- 'Predict' – you are not supposed to know the answer from memory but to deduce it, usually from information in the question
- 'Suggest' – this implies that there is more than one acceptable answer or that you are expected to arrive at the answer using your general knowledge of chemistry.

How to approach the examination

If the examination centre has provided a detailed timetable, then highlight your examinations and put the timetable in a prominent place in your home. Ask one of your family to check with you each day your commitments for the next day. This will avoid the type of situation exemplified by:

Student 'I thought that the examination was this afternoon.'
Teacher 'No, it was this morning, you will have to sit it in November or next year.'

Put out the correct equipment the night before – pencil, pencil sharpener, eraser, ruler, calculator (are the batteries OK?) and two pens.

Leave home in generous time; if you are late you will not be given extra time and under certain circumstances you may not be allowed to enter the examination room. The regulations vary depending on the Examination Board. Do not put yourself at a disadvantage. It is no use saying, for example, 'The 8.45 bus didn't run this morning and I had to wait for the 9.15'. It is the candidate's responsibility to arrive on time for the examination, and you should always allow time to spare.

Multiple choice papers

Attempt all of the questions – there are no penalties for incorrect responses.

Read the question carefully, remembering that at least one of the incorrect answers (called distractors) will seem to be correct. Never make a blind guess, but try to eliminate some of the incorrect answers and increase the odds in your favour. Do not rush – think.

If you cannot answer a question, or remain uncertain as to which is the correct answer, put a star by it, leave it and return to it when you have completed the other questions. Use any spare time at the end of the examination to check your answers.

Theory papers

Once the examination has started, flick through the paper and choose a question you feel confident about. You do not have to start with question 1. Read the question twice, look at the mark allocation for each part and then decide exactly what is required to be awarded the marks. This needs a disciplined approach; far too many candidates write at length without answering the question. Never forget – marks are not awarded for correct chemistry but for correct chemistry that answers the question.

- Follow the instructions in the question, being particularly careful to respond to words and phrases such as 'describe' and 'give a reason for'.
- Take reasonable care that your writing is legible – what cannot be read cannot be marked.
- Do not offer more alternative answers than required, in the vain hope that the examiner will pick out the correct ones.
- Avoid 'waffle', as this wastes your time. Similarly do not rewrite the information given in the question and expect to gain marks.
- Do not rush. This is a major cause of mistakes, particularly of misreading the question. The time allocated to the examination is adequate for candidates to complete the paper.
- Leave the hardest questions until last. Make sure you attempt all the questions.
- If you finish early, take the opportunity to check through your answers. Ask yourself, 'Have I answered the question and have I made sufficient points to be awarded the marks?'.

After the examination the papers are sent to the examiner allocated to your centre. This examiner will be part of a team headed by a Chief Examiner. All the members of the examining team will look at a sample of their scripts and assess the range of candidates' responses to each question. Then the team will meet to coordinate the marking. For each question, they will decide the range of responses that are acceptable. During the marking period, the Chief Examiner will sample the marking of each examiner, at least twice, to ensure comparability of marking across the team. The scripts and the marks are returned to the Examination Board where the minimum mark for each grade is decided. A few weeks later you are informed of your grade.

Practical examinations

There are three ways of assessing practical skills.

● **School-based assessment** A series of assessments are conducted throughout the course and should be an integral part of the teaching programme. The teachers will have received guidance and training about the conduct and content of these assessments. The following skills will be assessed:

C1 Using and organising techniques, apparatus and materials.
C2 Observing, recording and measuring.
C3 Handling experimental observations and data.
C4 Planning investigations.

Near the end of the course, the results of these assessments are sent to the Examination Board where they are moderated, to the same standard across all the centres.

● **Practical test** This is a single practical test set by the Examination Board and conducted at your centre. The procedures assessed are the same as those in the school-based assessment. You are given the tests for ions and gases. This paper is marked by external examiners.

● **Written test of practical skills** This a part of the final examination programme. It is a single written paper with a complete emphasis on laboratory procedures. The syllabus gives a full list of the required procedures, a selection of which is:

● recording readings from diagrams of apparatus
● completing tables of data
● drawing conclusions
● plotting graphs
● identifying sources of error and suggesting improvements in experimental procedures.

You are not given the tests for ions and gases. These papers are marked by a team of external examiners in the same way as the theory papers.

Preparation for practical assessment

The best preparation for the written test is to study some of the past papers, to become familiar with the type of question set. It is likely that the questions on your paper will be similar. Although it is a written test, the practical lessons at school will have provided both the skills and knowledge needed for this examination.

The two direct assessments of practical skills, that is, the school-based assessment and the practical test, present a different problem to a purely written assessment – in a word, nerves. In any examination you need to be calm and measured in your approach; this is easier to achieve in the written examination – a couple of deep breaths, pick a question you are confident about and 'off you go'. If you make a mistake you can just delete it and write the correct version (with a reference to the examiner) in a convenient place. This is not the case in practical work. If you make a mistake you will probably have to start the exercise again, if you have enough material! You will have wasted time and not improved your state of mind. When carpenters are being trained to cut pieces of wood to length they are told to 'measure twice then cut once'. In the context of a practical examination this translates to 'Think about what you are about to do, and when you are certain of the correct action then carry it out.' Do not rush.

How to improve your grade

Here are a few brief summary points, all of which have been mentioned elsewhere in this book.

- Use this book – it was written to help students attain high grades.
- Learn all the work. Low grades are nearly always attributable to inadequate preparation. If you can recall the work you will succeed; if you cannot you will fail. Harsh but true.
- Work to understand the chemistry. Many questions require both recall and understanding.
- Practise skills – calculations, equation writing and interpretation of graphs.
- Use past papers to reinforce revision, to become familiar with the type of question and to gain confidence.
- Answer the question as written on the paper. Do not accept a question as an invitation to write about the topic.

Answers

TOPIC 1

Sample question 3

Student's answer: The particles are arranged ✗ and held together by strong attractive forces. ✗ The particles move back and forth. ✗

Examiner's comments: No marks awarded. The responses have some merit but lack the precision to earn the marks.

Mark 1 – 'arranged' alone does not necessarily suggest order. 'They are arranged in a lattice or regular pattern' would have gained the mark.

Mark 2 – information about the attractive forces was not required by the question. 'Close together' would have been awarded this mark.

Mark 3 – 'the particles move back and forth about their position' would have been allocated the mark or, even better – 'they vibrate'.

TOPIC 2

● Try this

1 a) Using a locating agent. [1 mark]
   b) Ink will dissolve *or* it will produce spots on the chromatogram *or* pencil will not dissolve. [1 mark]
   c) R_f = 0.25 (accept 0.22 to 0.28) [1 mark]
   d) 3.3 cm above the datum line (accept 3.1 to 3.5). [1 mark]
   e) No glutamic acid, no tyrosine, more taurine, slightly more cysteic acid, slightly less glycine. [Any three for 3 marks]

TOPIC 3

● Try this

1 $^{7}_{3}$Li 3 protons 3 electrons 4 neutrons [1 mark]
   $^{65}_{30}$Zn 30 protons 30 electrons 35 neutrons [1 mark]
   $^{108}_{47}$Ag 47 protons 47 electrons 61 neutrons [1 mark]
2 21p + 21e + 24n = 66 [1 mark]
3 9p + 9e = 18 [1 mark]
4 Fe 2,8,14,2 [1 mark]
   As 2,8,18,5 [1 mark]
   Sr 2,8,18,8,2 [1 mark]
   Pd 2,8,18,16,2 [1 mark]
5 Cs 1 [1 mark]
   Ra 2 [1 mark]
   Ge 4 [1 mark]
   At 7 [1 mark]

6 a) The only difference is the number of neutrons. [1 mark]
   b) Three common features are the same number of protons, same number of electrons and same electronic structure. [3 marks]

7

Atom	Number of protons	Number of neutrons	Number of electrons
$^{19}_{9}$F	9	10	9
$^{9}_{4}$Be	4	5	4
$^{23}_{11}$Na	11	12	11
$^{27}_{13}$Al	13	14	13
$^{48}_{22}$Ti	22	26	22
$^{127}_{53}$I	53	74	53

[Each correct entry 1 mark]

8 i) Li 2,1 ii) B 2,3 iii) N 2,5 iv) Ne 2,8
   v) Mg 2,8,2 vi) Si 2,8,4 vii) S 2,8,6
   viii) Cl 2,8,7 ix) Ar 2,8,8 x) Ca 2,8,8,2
   [10 marks]

TOPIC 4

● Try this

1 I$^-$, Cs$^+$, Se^{2-}, Ba^{2+}, P^{3-} [5 marks]
2 i) $^{9}_{4}$Be^{2+} 4 protons 2 electrons 5 neutrons [1 mark]
   ii) $^{55}_{25}$Mn^{2+} 25 protons 23 electrons 30 neutrons [1 mark]
   iii) $^{70}_{31}$Ga^{3+} 31 protons 28 electrons 39 neutrons [1 mark]
   iv) $^{75}_{33}$As^{3-} 33 protons 36 electrons 42 neutrons [1 mark]
   v) $^{80}_{35}$Br$^-$ 35 protons 36 electrons 45 neutrons [1 mark]
3 i) potassium fluoride

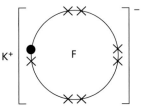

[2 marks]

   ii) calcium sulphide

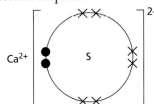

[2 marks]

iii) lithium oxide

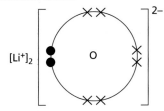

[3 marks]

iv) aluminium fluoride

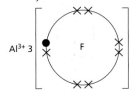 *or*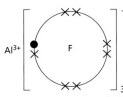

[3 marks]

4 **i)** bromine 1 [1 mark]
   ii) arsenic 3 [1 mark]
   iii) germanium 4 [1 mark]
   iv) tellurium 2 [1 mark]
   v) phosphorus 3 [1 mark]

5 **i)** hydrogen fluoride HF [1 mark]
   ii) nitrogen chloride NCl_3 [1 mark]
   iii) germanium oxide GeO_2 [1 mark]
   iv) phosphorus nitride PN [1 mark]
   v) oxygen fluoride OF_2 or F_2O [1 mark]

6 **i)** ammonia NH_3

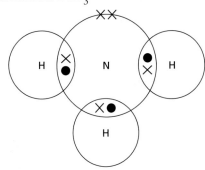

[2 marks]

ii) silicon hydride

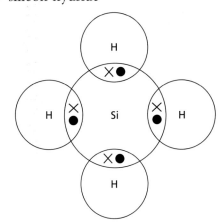

[3 marks]

iii) oxygen molecule O_2

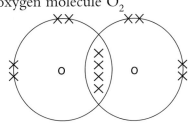

[2 marks]

iv) phosphorus fluoride

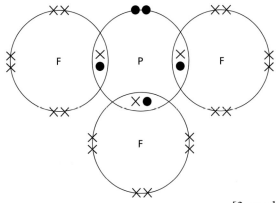

[3 marks]

v) hydrogen sulphide

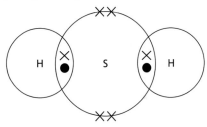

[3 marks]

TOPIC 5

● Try this

1 **i)** lithium iodide LiI [1 mark]
   ii) sodium oxide Na_2O [1 mark]
   iii) boron fluoride BF_3 [1 mark]
   iv) calcium nitride Ca_3N_2 [1 mark]
   v) germanium chloride $GeCl_4$ [1 mark]
   vi) arsenic oxide As_2O_3 [1 mark]
   vii) aluminium sulphide Al_2S_3 [1 mark]
   viii) silicon carbide SiC [1 mark]

2 **i)** sodium sulphate Na_2SO_4 [1 mark]
   ii) aluminium hydroxide $Al(OH)_3$ [1 mark]
   iii) calcium nitrate $Ca(NO_3)_2$ [1 mark]
   iv) magnesium carbonate $MgCO_3$ [1 mark]
   v) calcium phosphate $Ca_3(PO_4)_2$ [1 mark]

3 **i)** $C_2H_4O_2$ [1 mark]
   ii) C_4H_{10} [1 mark]
   iii) $C_4H_8O_2$ [1 mark]
   iv) $C_4H_{10}O$ [1 mark]
   v) $C_2H_4Cl_2$ [1 mark]

4 i) $2Na + Cl_2 \rightarrow 2NaCl$ [1 mark]
ii) $2Ca + O_2 \rightarrow 2CaO$ [1 mark]
iii) $2Fe + 3Br_2 \rightarrow 2FeBr_3$ [1 mark]
iv) $4Li + O_2 \rightarrow 2Li_2O$ [1 mark]
v) $4P + 3O_2 \rightarrow 2P_2O_3$ [1 mark]
vi) $MgO + 2HCl \rightarrow MgCl_2 + H_2O$ [1 mark]
vii) $2Na + 2H_2O \rightarrow 2NaOH + H_2$ [1 mark]
viii) $FeCl_3 + 3NaOH \rightarrow Fe(OH)_3 + 3NaCl$ [1 mark]

5 i) $2K + Br_2 \rightarrow 2KBr$ [2 marks]
ii) $2Al + 3I_2 \rightarrow 2AlI_3$ [2 marks]
iii) $4Na + O_2 \rightarrow 2Na_2O$ [2 marks]
iv) $MgCl_2 + 2NaOH \rightarrow Mg(OH)_2 + 2NaCl$ [2 marks]
v) $Ca + 2HCl \rightarrow CaCl_2 + H_2$ [2 marks]

TOPIC 6

● Try this

1 i) 30 **ii)** 106 **iii)** 102 **iv)** 74 **v)** 78 [5 marks]

2 i) 18 g **ii)** 44 g **iii)** 40 g **iv)** 84 g **v)** 250 g [5 marks]

3 i) $2 \times 18 = 36$ g [2 marks]
ii) $3 \times 28 = 84$ g [2 marks]
iii) $0.5 \times 40 = 20$ g [2 marks]
iv) $0.125 \times 40 = 5.0$ g [2 marks]
v) $0.7 \times 80 = 5.6$ g [2 marks]

4 $\frac{20}{16}$ moles of $CH_4 = 1.25$ [1 mark]
1.25×2 moles of $O_2 = 2.5$ (see mole ratio in equation) [1 mark]
mass of oxygen $= 2.5 \times 32 = 80$ g [1 mark]

5 $\frac{5}{80}$ moles of $CuO = 0.0625$ [1 mark]
0.0625 moles of $CuSO_4$ formed [1 mark]
mass of copper(II) sulphate $= 0.0625 \times 160 = 10$ g [1 mark]

6 i) 2 [1 mark]
ii) 0.05 [1 mark]
iii) 40 [1 mark]
iv) 0.15 [1 mark]
v) $1200\,cm^3 = 1.2\,dm^3$; $\frac{1.2}{24} = 0.05$ [1 mark]

7 i) $\frac{1.6}{32} = 0.05$; $0.05 \times 24 = 1.2\,dm^3$ [2 marks]
ii) $\frac{320}{32} = 10$; $10 \times 24 = 240\,dm^3$ [2 marks]
iii) $\frac{4.8}{32} = 0.15$; $0.15 \times 24 = 3.6\,dm^3$ [2 marks]
iv) $\frac{8}{32} = 0.25$; $0.25 \times 24 = 6\,dm^3$ [2 marks]
v) $\frac{40}{32} = 1.25$; $1.25 \times 24 = 30\,dm^3$ [2 marks]

8 Moles of $C_4H_8 = 0.025$ [1 mark]
Moles of $CO_2 = 0.025 \times 4$ (from mole ratio in equation) $= 0.1$ [1 mark]
$0.1 \times 24 = 2.4\,dm^3$ [1 mark]

9 The mole ratio from the equation is $2C_2H_6 : 7O_2$. [1 mark]
The volume ratio must be the same.
$20\,cm^3$ ethane will react with $\frac{7}{2} \times 20 = 70\,cm^3$ oxygen. [1 mark]

10 $Fe_2(SO_4)_3 \rightarrow Fe_2O_3 + 3SO_3$
M_r of $Fe_2(SO_4)_3 = 400$ [1 mark]
Moles of $Fe_2(SO_4)_3 = \frac{20}{400} = 0.05$ [1 mark]
Moles of $SO_3 = 0.05 \times 3 = 0.15$ (from mole ratio in equation) [1 mark]
Volume of $SO_3 = 0.15 \times 24 = 3.6\,dm^3$ [1 mark]

11 $2Al + 6HCl \rightarrow 2AlCl_3 + 3H_2$
Moles of hydrogen formed $= \frac{0.72}{24} = 0.03$ [1 mark]
Moles of aluminium used $= 0.03 \times \frac{2}{3} = 0.02$ (from mole ratio $Al : H_2$) [1 mark]
Mass of aluminium used $= 0.02 \times 27 = 0.54$ g [1 mark]

12

Element	carbon	hydrogen	oxygen	
Percentage	38.7	9.67	51.6	
Mole ratio by atoms	$\frac{38.7}{12}$ $= 3.225$	$\frac{9.67}{1}$ $= 9.67$	$\frac{51.6}{16}$ $= 3.225$	[1 mark]
Simplest mole ratio	$\frac{3.225}{3.225}$ $=1$	$\frac{9.67}{3.225}$ $= 3$	$\frac{3.225}{3.225}$ $= 1$	[1 mark]

Empirical formula is $C_1H_3O_1$, written as CH_3O ($M_r = 31$). [1 mark]
Molecular formula, since $\frac{62}{31} = 2$, is $C_2H_6O_2$. [1 mark]

13 i) 2 g in $100\,cm^3$ so 20 g in $1000\,cm^3$ [1 mark]
$\frac{20}{40} = 0.5$ mol so concentration $= 0.5\,mol/dm^3$ [1 mark]
ii) 50 g in $1000\,cm^3$ [1 mark];
$\frac{50}{40} = 1.25\,mol/dm^3$ [1 mark]
iii) 100 g in $1000\,cm^3$ [1 mark];
$\frac{100}{40} = 2.5\,mol/dm^3$ [1 mark]

14 i) M_r of $KOH = 56$ [1 mark]; moles of $KOH = 0.5 \times 0.1 = 0.05$ [1 mark]
Mass of $KOH = 0.05 \times 56 = 2.8$ g [1 mark]
ii) M_r of $Na_2CO_3 = 106$ [1 mark]; moles of $Na_2CO_3 = 0.1 \times 0.05 = 0.005$ [1 mark]
Mass of $Na_2CO_3 = 0.005 \times 106 = 0.53$ g [1 mark]
iii) M_r of $NaCl = 58.5$ [1 mark];
moles of $NaCl = 2.5 \times 3 = 7.5$ [1 mark]
Mass of $NaCl = 7.5 \times 58.5 = 438.75$ g [1 mark]

15 Moles of Na_2CO_3 = volume (dm^3) × concentration (mol/dm^3)

= 0.025 × 0.10

= 0.0025   [1 mark]

Moles of HCl = 0.0025 × 2 = 0.005 (from mole ratio in equation) [1 mark]

Concentration of HCl = moles/volume (dm^3)

$= \frac{0.005}{0.031}$

= 0.16 mol/dm^3

[1 mark]

16 $CH_3COOH + C_2H_5OH \rightarrow$

$\qquad CH_3COOC_2H_5 + H_2O$

1 mole	1 mole
$M_r = 60$	$M_r = 88$ [1 mark]
$\frac{12}{60} = 0.2$	0.2 moles is the theoretical yield [1 mark]
	0.2 × 88 = 17.6 g [1 mark]

Percentage yield $= \frac{7.2 \times 100}{17.6} = 40.9\%$ [1 mark]

17 $NiO + 2HCl \rightarrow NiCl_2 + H_2O$

$NiCl_2 + 6H_2O \rightarrow NiCl_2.6H_2O$

2 moles HCl form 1 mole $NiCl_2.6H_2O$

[1 mark]

$\frac{1.6 \times 50}{1000} = 0.08$ moles HCl [1 mark]

form 0.04 moles $NiCl_2.6H_2O$ [1 mark]

Theoretical yield = 0.04 × 238 = 9.52 g

[1 mark]

Percentage yield $= \frac{6.1 \times 100}{9.52} = 64.1\%$

[1 mark]

18 $2NaHCO_3 \rightarrow Na_2CO_3 + CO_2 + H_2O$

2 moles	1 mole
$M_r = 84$	$M_r = 44$ [1 mark]

$\frac{2.24}{44} = 0.051$ moles of CO_2 [1 mark]

are formed from 2 × 0.051 = 0.102 moles of $NaHCO_3$ [1 mark]

Mass of pure sodium hydrogencarbonate = 0.102 × 84 = 8.57 g [1 mark]

Percentage purity $= \frac{8.57 \times 100}{9.30} = 92.2\%$

[1 mark]

TOPIC 7

● Try this

1 The three products are hydrogen, iodine, potassium hydroxide. [3 marks]

At the cathode: K^+(aq) and H^+(aq)

$\qquad\qquad 2H^+ + 2e^- \rightarrow H_2$ [1 mark]

At the anode I^-(aq) and OH^-(aq)

$\qquad\qquad 2I^- - 2e^- \rightarrow I_2$ [1 mark]

In solution there are K^+(aq) and OH^-(aq); this is potassium hydroxide, an alkali. [1 mark]

2 The anode is copper. [1 mark]

The cathode is the nickel spoon. [1 mark]

The electrolyte is copper sulphate or any soluble copper salt. [1 mark]

The equation for the anode reaction is $Cu - 2e^- \rightarrow Cu^{2+}$ or $Cu \rightarrow Cu^{2+} + 2e^-$

[1 mark]

The equation for the cathode reaction is $Cu^{2+} + 2e^- \rightarrow Cu$ [1 mark]

TOPIC 9

● Try this

1 a) Either a higher temperature or a catalyst added. [1 mark]

Examiner's comment: 'Powdered magnesium' is not an acceptable reason, as the question states that the pieces of magnesium are identical.

Examiner's tip

▶ 'Suggest' in a question means that it is not asking for recall – you need to come up with an idea!

---

b) Experiment 3: double concentration, double the rate so half the time taken = 30 seconds. [1 mark]

Experiment 4: four times slower, concentration of acid = 0.25 mol/dm^3.

[1 mark]

2 Do experiment without catalyst. [1 mark]

Collect oxygen in a gas syringe. [1 mark]

Measure volume at regular time intervals and calculate rate of uncatalysed reaction. [1 mark]

Weigh catalyst. [1 mark]

Repeat experiment using catalyst, keeping all other variables (volume, concentration of solution, temperature) the same. [1 mark]

Calculate rate of catalysed reaction. [1 mark]

Filter off catalyst (wash, dry) and weigh.

[1 mark]

Show that the rate is faster with the catalyst and that the mass of catalyst is the same.

[1 mark]

3 a) Where light hit the paper, silver(I) bromide changed to silver, this appearing grey. [1 mark]

Where no light hit the paper, there is still silver(I) bromide, which is white. [1 mark]

b) It would all go grey [1 mark] because it is all exposed to light, allowing the reaction changing silver(I) bromide to silver. [1 mark]

c) $Ag^+ + e^- \rightarrow Ag$ [1 mark]

d) Lighter grey, or a longer time to turn grey [1 mark] because the rate of reaction would be slower. [1 mark]

TOPIC 10

● Try this

1 Equilibrium 1: no change [1 mark] because number of molecules same on both sides. [1 mark]
Equilibrium 2: moves to right [1 mark] because 3 molecules form 2 molecules. [1 mark]
Equilibrium 3: moves to left [1 mark] because 1 molecule forms 2 molecules. [1 mark]

2 Carbon dioxide can escape so equilibrium moves to right [1 mark] and all calcium carbonate decomposes. [1 mark]

3 **i)** Position of equilibrium unchanged. [1 mark]
ii) Moves to right, or more methanol. [1 mark]
iii) Moves to right, or more methanol. [1 mark]
iv) Moves to left, or less methanol. [1 mark]

4 **i)** More yellow solid; brown liquid disappears. [2 marks]
ii) Yellow solid disappears; more brown liquid. [2 marks]
iii) More yellow solid; right-hand side has smaller volume (no gases). [2 marks]
iv) Exothermic. [1 mark]
Back reaction is favoured by increase in temperature so it is endothermic; forward must be exothermic. [1 mark]

5 **i)** Darker. [1 mark]
Moves to left to remove additional Br^- from KBr. [1 mark]
ii) Darker. [1 mark]
Moves to left to remove additional H^+ from HCl. [1 mark]
iii) Lighter. [1 mark]
Moves to right to replace H^+ [1 mark] which was neutralised by alkali.

TOPIC 11

● Try this

1 **i)** $2Al + Fe_2O_3 \rightarrow 2Fe + Al_2O_3$ [2 marks] [Only 1 mark if not balanced]
ii) Fe_2O_3 [1 mark] because it oxidised Al to Al_2O_3 *or* because it gave oxygen to Al. [1 mark]
iii) Fe_2O_3 to 2Fe [1 mark] because it lost oxygen. [1 mark]

2 $PbO_2 + 2H_2 \rightarrow Pb + 2H_2O$ [2 marks] [Only 1 mark if not balanced]
$2H_2$ to $2H_2O$ is oxidation. [1 mark]
The oxidant is lead(IV)oxide. [1 mark]

3 $Cl_2 + 2I^- \rightarrow 2Cl^- + I_2$
$Cl_2 + 2e^- \rightarrow 2Cl^-$ [1 mark]
$2I^- - 2e^- \rightarrow I_2$ [1 mark]
The change involving iodide ions is oxidation [1 mark] because the iodide ions have lost electrons. [1 mark]
The reducing agent is the iodide ion, I^- [1 mark] because it lost electrons to the chlorine molecule, which gained electrons and was reduced. [1 mark]

4 **i)** Reduction [1 mark] because the oxidation state has decreased.
ii) Oxidation [1 mark] because the oxidation state has increased.
iii) Reduction [1 mark] because the oxidation state has decreased.
iv) Neither [1 mark] because the oxidation state has not changed.

5 **a)** Valency of silver is 1. [1 mark]
Formula of ion is Ag^+. [1 mark]
b) Valency of magnesium is 2. [1 mark]
Formula of ion is Mg^{2+}. [1 mark]
c) $Mg + 2Ag^+ \rightarrow Mg^{2+} + 2Ag$ [2 marks] [Only 1 mark if not balanced]
d) $2Ag^+ + 2e^- \rightarrow 2Ag$ *or* $Ag^+ + e^- \rightarrow Ag$ [1 mark]
e) Mg [1 mark] because it gave electrons to the silver ions. [1 mark]

TOPIC 12

● Try this

1 Weakly alkaline 11, neutral 7, strongly acidic 1, strongly alkaline 13, weakly acidic 5. [5 marks]

2 zinc carbonate + nitric acid $\rightarrow$
zinc nitrate + carbon dioxide + water [1 mark]
$Ca(OH)_2 + 2HCl \rightarrow CaCl_2 + CO_2 + H_2O$ [1 mark]

$ZnO + 2H^+ \rightarrow Zn^{2+} + H_2O$ [1 mark]

lithium + hydrochloric acid →
 lithium chloride + hydrogen [1 mark]

$Mg(OH)_2 + H_2SO_4 \rightarrow MgSO_4 + 2H_2O$
[1 mark]

$NH_4NO_3 + NaOH \rightarrow$
$NaNO_3 + NH_3 + H_2O$ [1 mark]

3 a) i) Zinc + chloric(VII) acid →
zinc chlorate(VII) + hydrogen [1 mark for
each product]

ii) Potassium hydroxide + chloric(VII) acid
→ potassium chlorate(VII) + water [1 mark
for each product]

iii) $Mg + 2HClO_4 \rightarrow Mg(ClO_4)_2 + H_2$
[2 marks]

iv) $Mg(OH)_2 + 2HClO_4 \rightarrow Mg(ClO_4)_2 + 2H_2O$
[2 marks]

v) $Na_2CO_3 + 2HClO_4 \rightarrow 2NaClO_4 + CO_2 + H_2O$
[2 marks]

vi) $ZnO + 2HClO_4 \rightarrow Zn(ClO_4)_2 + H_2O$
[2 marks]

vii) $CaCO_3 + 2HClO_4 \rightarrow Ca(ClO_4)_2 + CO_2 + H_2O$
[2 marks]
[For each symbol equation only 1 mark if
not balanced.]

b) $H^+ + OH^- \rightarrow H_2O$ [1 mark]
Examiner's comment: It is the same equation
for any strong acid with any strong base.

c) Same length of magnesium ribbon.
[1 mark]
Time until all reacted. [1 mark]
Same concentration of aqueous acids.
[1 mark]
Same volume of aqueous solution. [1 mark]
Same temperature. [1 mark]
Chloric(VII) acid reacts faster or takes less
time. [1 mark]

4 a) All above 7. [1 mark]

b) Sodium hydrogencarbonate the lowest;
sodium hydroxide the highest. [2 marks]

5 Cause of low pH probably acid rain. [1 mark]
Calcium carbonate better [1 mark] because it
is insoluble in water. [1 mark]
Calcium oxide is soluble so pH would go
above 7. [1 mark]

TOPIC 13
● **Try this**

1 a) Use excess to neutralise all the acid.
[1 mark]

b) Filter to remove excess or unreacted
nickel carbonate. [1 mark]

c) Partially evaporate because pure or better
crystals will form *or* because the crystals
contain water (they are hydrated). [1 mark]

d) The crystals are dried with the filter paper.
[1 mark]

2 i) Silver nitrate and sodium bromide.
[2 marks] (Silver bromide is an insoluble salt.)

ii) Copper(II) oxide, or hydroxide or
carbonate, and nitric acid. [2 marks]

iii) Potassium hydroxide, or carbonate, and
sulphuric acid. [2 marks]

iv) Calcium chloride, or nitrate, and any
soluble sulphate, e.g. sodium sulphate.
[2 marks] (Calcium sulphate is insoluble.)

v) Zinc metal, or oxide or hydroxide or
carbonate, and hydrochloric acid. [2 marks]

vi) Lithium hydroxide, or carbonate, and
hydrochloric acid. [2 marks]

3 C G F E B A D [3 marks]

4 sulphate, precipitate or residue, filtered or
centrifuged, soluble, heated [5 marks]

TOPIC 14
Sample question
Student's answer: It is zinc ✓ sulphate. ✓
Examiner's comment: Correct. The full 2 marks
awarded.

TOPIC 15
● **Try this**

1 a) Calcium [1 mark] because it is a metal.
[1 mark]

b) calcium + hydrochloric acid →
calcium chloride + hydrogen [2 marks]
phosphorus + hydrochloric acid →
no reaction [1 mark]

c) Measure pH or add pH paper. [1 mark]
Results: calcium oxide – high pH (10–14);
phosphorus oxide – low pH (1–3). [1 mark]
Litmus paper turns blue in calcium oxide and
red in phosphorus oxide. [1 mark]

2 a) Dull, brittle, poor conductor of heat, poor
conductor of electricity, not sonorous, not
ductile. [Any three for 3 marks]

b) 6 [1 mark]

c) $SeCl_2$ [1 mark]

d) Covalent [1 mark] because selenium is a
non-metal. [1 mark]

3 a) 2 + 8 + 18 + 4 [1 mark]

b) Germanium [1 mark] because it is a semi-
conductor *or* elements become more metallic
down the group. [1 mark]

c) i) GeF_4 **ii)** GeO_2 [2 marks]
d) Reacts with acids or named acid. [1 mark]
Reacts with alkalis or named alkali. [1 mark]
e) Germanium has higher melting point or boiling point. [1 mark]
Germanium is harder. [1 mark]

4 a) i) 139 particles [1 mark]
ii) 82 neutrons [1 mark]
iii) La^{3+} [1 mark]
b) i) $LaBr_3$ **ii)** La_2O_3 **iii)** LaN [3 marks]
c) i) High melting or boiling point, hard, good conductor of heat or electricity, shiny, malleable, ductile, sonorous.
[Any three for 3 marks]
ii) Reducing agent, reacts with dilute acids, oxide basic or amphoteric, forms positive ions, forms ionic chloride.
[Any two for 2 marks]
d) i) lanthanum + hydrochloric acid $\rightarrow$ lanthanum chloride + hydrogen
[1 mark for each product]
ii) $2La + 6HCl \rightarrow 2LaCl_3 + 3H_2$
[2 marks] [Only 1 mark if not balanced]

TOPIC 16
● Try this

1 Rubidium would move across water, melt, and hydrogen would ignite. [3 marks]
$2Rb + 2H_2O \rightarrow 2RbOH + H_2$ [2 marks]
Examiner's comment: If the products in the equation are correct but the equation is not correctly balanced, 1 mark. No marks if Rb_2O is written.

2 Li 181 °C Na 98 °C K 64 °C Rb ? Cs 29 °C
Average of K and Cs = 47 °C
Examiner's comment and marks: A better estimate is based on the fact that the difference between the melting points is decreasing down the group. The difference between K and Cs is 35 degrees. The difference between K and Rb should be bigger (e.g. 23 degrees) than the difference between rubidium and caesium (e.g. 12 degrees). Note the two differences in temperature must add up to 35 degrees.
[For average of 47 °C, 1 mark only. For melting point between 45 and 37 °C with some reasoning, 2 marks.]

> **Examiner's tip**
> ▶ Always explain your reasoning to the examiner. You have everything to gain.

3 a) At_2 [1 mark]
b) Solid, black. [2 marks]
c) $CaAt_2$ [1 mark]
d) Iodine and potassium astatide [1 mark] because reactivity increases up the group *or* iodine is more reactive than astatine. [1 mark]

4 a) $F_2 + 2Cl^- \rightarrow 2F^- + Cl_2$ [2 marks]
b) $F_2 + 2e^- \rightarrow 2F^-$ This is reduction, since fluorine has gained electrons (OILRIG again!)
[2 marks]
$2Cl^- \rightarrow 2e^- + Cl_2$ The chloride ion is the reducing agent, since it has given electrons to the fluorine molecules and reduced them.
[2 marks]

5 a) To prevent reaction with filament. [1 mark]
b) Hydrogen can burn or explode [1 mark] but helium does not. [1 mark]
c) Noble gases have complete outer energy level [1 mark] and do not form bonds. [1 mark] Other elements have incomplete outer levels [1 mark] and need to bond to fill outer level. [1 mark]
d) 40/24 [1 mark] = $1.67 \, g/dm^3$ [1 mark]

6 a) Barium [1 mark]
b) i) magnesium + water (or steam) $\rightarrow$ magnesium oxide + hydrogen
[1 mark for each product]
ii) $Ca + 2H_2O \rightarrow Ca(OH)_2 + H_2$
[2 marks] [Only 1 mark if not balanced]
iii) $Sr + 2HCl \rightarrow SrCl_2 + H_2$ [2 marks]
[Only 1 mark if not balanced]
c)

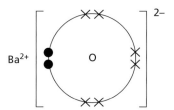

[3 marks]
[1 mark for correct charges, 1 mark for 1:1 ratio Ba to O, 1 mark for 6 + 2 electrons around oxygen]

TOPIC 17
● Try this
1 Physical differences:
● manganese has the higher melting point
● manganese is harder than magnesium
● manganese has the higher density. [Any two for 2 marks]

Chemical differences:
- magnesium is the more reactive metal
- magnesium has only one oxidation state, manganese has more than one oxidation state
- magnesium compounds are white, manganese forms coloured compounds
- magnesium and its compounds do not show any catalytic activity, manganese metal or its compounds can behave as catalysts. [Any two for 2 marks]

> **Examiner's tip**
> ▶ Note the comparison in all these statements. It is essential.

TOPIC 20
● Try this

1 Measure its boiling point (100 °C) or its freezing point (0 °C). [2 marks]

2 Domestic uses include washing, laundry, cooking. [3 marks]
Industrial uses include cooling in power stations, agriculture, steel making. [3 marks]

3 From leaded petrol (lead in paints is also acceptable) [1 mark]; damage to brain and central nervous system, especially in children [1 mark]; use unleaded petrol (and paints that do not contain lead). [1 mark]

4 Tube 1: nails will rust – oxygen in air and water present. [1 mark]
Tube 2: nails will not rust – oxygen in air present but no water. [1 mark]
Tube 3: nails will not rust – water present but no oxygen. [1 mark]
Tube 4: nails will rust – oxygen and water present. [1 mark]

5 a) Coal, natural gas and petroleum or oil. [3 marks]
   b) Wood, animal dung, peat, alcohol. [Any two for 2 marks]
   c) $C_3H_8 + 5O_2 \rightarrow 3CO_2 + 4H_2O$ [2 marks]

6 $C_6H_{12}O_6 + 6O_2 \rightarrow 6CO_2 + 6H_2O$ [1 mark]
Examiner's comment: Do not forget that there are six oxygen atoms in the glucose.

7 zinc carbonate + nitric acid →
   zinc nitrate + carbon dioxide + water [2 marks]
$MgCO_3 + H_2SO_4 \rightarrow MgSO_4 + CO_2 + H_2O$ [2 marks]
$NiCO_3 + 2H^+ \rightarrow Ni^{2+} + CO_2 + H_2O$ [2 marks]

8 a) $2CH_4 + 3O_2 \rightarrow 2CO + 4H_2O$ [2 marks]
   [Only 1 mark if not balanced]
   b) To prevent formation of carbon monoxide. [1 mark] which is poisonous. [1 mark]

9 a) $M_r = 132$ [1 mark] 28/132 = 21.2% [1 mark]
   $M_r = 80$ [1 mark] 28/80 = 35% [1 mark]
   $M_r = 60$ [1 mark] 28/60 = 46.7% [1 mark]
   b) i) $Ca_3(PO_4)_2$ [1 mark]
   ii) Contains both nitrogen and phosphorus. [1 mark]
   iii) Potassium [1 mark]

TOPIC 21
● Try this

1 a) i) Nitric acid [1 mark]
   ii) $KNO_3 \rightarrow KNO_2 + O_2$
   [1 mark for unbalanced equation]
   $2KNO_3 \rightarrow 2KNO_2 + O_2$
   [2 marks for balanced equation]
   b) i) The acid is pure and cheap *or* in the old process the acid is impure and expensive. [1 mark]
   ii) Sulphur beds in USA or Poland or Mexico, or from natural gas. [1 mark]
   iii) Vanadium oxide or vanadium(V) oxide [1 mark]
   iv) Decrease in temperature favours exothermic reaction. [1 mark]
   Equilibrium to right *or* less sulphur trioxide *or* lower yield. [1 mark]
   v) Add to concentrated sulphuric acid [1 mark] then add water. [1 mark]
   vi) Making detergents, batteries, pickling metals, making paint, dyes, making fibres, making fertilisers, in petroleum industry. [2 marks]
   c) i) Number of moles of H_2SO_4 in 25 cm^3 of 2.0 mol/dm^3 = 0.025 × 2 = 0.05 [1 mark]
   ii) Maximum number of moles of $CuSO_4.5H_2O$ that could be formed = 0.05 [1 mark]
   iii) Maximum mass of $CuSO_4.5H_2O$ that could be formed = 12.5 g [1 mark]
   iv) Percentage yield = $\frac{7.3}{12.5} \times 100$ = 58.4% [1 mark]

TOPIC 22

● Try this

1 **a)** solid **X**: calcium oxide [1 mark]
   solid **Y**: calcium hydroxide [1 mark]
   precipitate **Z**: calcium carbonate [1 mark]
   b) $CaO + H_2O \rightarrow Ca(OH)_2$ [2 marks]
   $Ca(OH)_2 + CO_2 \rightarrow CaCO_3 + H_2O$ [2 marks]
   $CaCO_3 \rightarrow CaO + CO_2$ [2 marks]

2 **a)** $CaO + 2H^+ \rightarrow Ca^{2+} + H_2O$ [2 marks]
   b) i) pH = 7 [1 mark]
   ii) pH above 7 [1 mark]

TOPIC 23

● Try this

1 **A** is an alcohol, **B** is an alkene, **C** is an organic acid, **D** is an alkane, **E** is an ester, **F** is a chloroalkane. [6 marks]

2 **i)** methanoic acid + zinc →
       zinc methanoate + hydrogen [2 marks]
   ii) propanoic acid + copper(II) oxide →
       copper(II) propanoate + water [2 marks]
   iii) butanoic acid + sodium carbonate →
       sodium butanoate + carbon dioxide + water
       [2 marks]
   iv) butene + bromine → dibromobutane
       [2 marks]
   v) ethanoic acid + butanol →
       butyl ethanoate + water [2 marks]
   vi) pentene + hydrogen → pentane
       [2 marks]
   vii) propene + water → propanol [2 marks]
   viii) ethane + chlorine →
       chloroethane + hydrogen chloride [2 marks]
   ix) propanol + oxygen (excess) →
       carbon dioxide and water [2 marks]
   x) methanoic acid + propanol →
       propyl methanoate [2 marks]

3 **i)** $NaOH + CH_3CH_2COOH \rightarrow$
       $CH_3CH_2COONa + H_2O$ [2 marks]
   ii) $2HCOOH + Mg \rightarrow (HCOO)_2Mg + H_2$
       [2 marks]
   iii) $Na_2CO_3 + 2CH_3CH_2CH_2COOH \rightarrow$
       $2CH_3CH_2CH_2COONa + CO_2 + H_2O$
       [2 marks]
   iv) $2CH_4 + 3O_2 \rightarrow 2CO + 4H_2O$ [2 marks]
   v) $CH_3COOH + CH_3OH \rightarrow$
       $CH_3COOCH_3 + H_2O$ [2 marks]
   vi) $C_3H_6 + Br_2 \rightarrow C_3H_6Br_2$ [2 marks]

4 **i)** $C_8H_{18} \rightarrow C_4H_{10} + 2C_2H_4$ [2 marks]
   ii) $C_7H_{16} \rightarrow C_5H_{12} + C_2H_4$ [2 marks]
   iii) $C_9H_{20} \rightarrow C_6H_{12} + C_3H_6 + H_2$ [2 marks]

TOPIC 24

● Try this

1 **i)**

[1 mark]

   ii)

[1 mark]

2 **i)**

[1 mark]

   ii)

[1 mark]

3 $-(HN(CH_2)_6NHOC(CH_2)_4CO)_n-$
   [2 marks]

4 **a)** Amide or polypeptide. [1 mark]

   b)

different monomers
[1 mark]

amide linkage
[1 mark]

evidence of chain
or continuation
[1 mark]

[3 marks]

   c) Polyester, or named polyester such as terylene. [1 mark]

Index

Periodic table of the elements

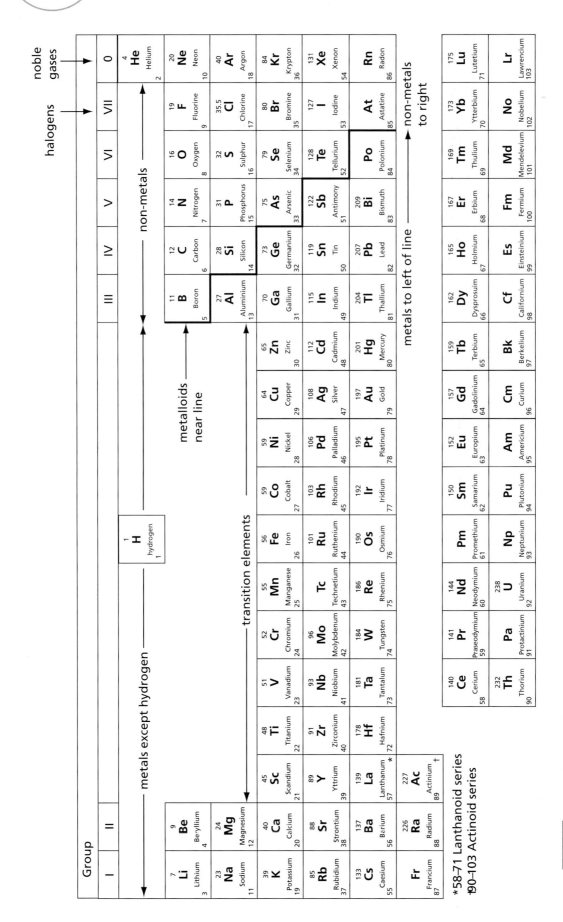